XIX

PUBLIC ROADS & CANALS

LIBRARY OF
EARLY AMERICAN BUSINESS AND INDUSTRY

REPORT

OF THE

SECRETARY OF THE TREASURY

[ALBERT GALLATIN]

ON THE SUBJECT OF

PUBLIC ROADS & CANALS

[1808]

REPRINTS OF ECONOMIC CLASSICS

AUGUSTUS M. KELLEY · PUBLISHERS
NEW YORK 1968

First Edition 1808

(Washington: Printed by R. C. Weightman.
By Order of the Senate, April 12, 1808)

Reprinted 1968 by

AUGUSTUS M. KELLEY · PUBLISHERS

NEW YORK NEW YORK 10010

PRINTED IN THE UNITED STATES OF AMERICA
by SENTRY PRESS, NEW YORK, N. Y. 10019

REPORT

OF THE

SECRETARY OF THE TREASURY,

ON THE SUBJECT OF

PUBLIC ROADS AND CANALS;

MADE

IN PURSUANCE OF A RESOLUTION OF SENATE,

OF MARCH 2, 1807.

APRIL 12, 1808.

PRINTED BY ORDER OF THE SENATE.

WASHINGTON:

PRINTED BY R. C. WEIGHTMAN,

. . . .

1808.

IN SENATE

OF

THE UNITED STATES.

APRIL 12th, 1808.

Mr. ADAMS, from the committee appointed on the subject of public roads and canals, reported, that 1200 copies of the following papers, be printed for the use of the Senate :

Resolution of Senate, of 2d March, 1807,
A letter from the secretary of the treasury;
Report of same ;
Circular queries of the same ;
Mr. Latrobe's communication marked E ; and
Mr. Fulton's letter marked F.

Resolved, That the secretary of the treasury be directed to prepare and report to the Senate, at their next session, a plan for the application of such means as are within the power of Congress, to the purposes of opening roads, and making canals; together with a statement of the undertakings, of that nature, which as objects of public improvement, may require and deserve the aid of government; and also a statement of works of the nature mentioned, which have been commenced, the progress which has been made in them, and the means and prospect of their being completed; and such information as, in the opinion of the secretary, shall be material, in relation to the objects of this resolution.

Attest,

SAMUEL A. OTIS, *Secretary.*

TREASURY DEPARTMENT,

April 4th, 1808.

SIR,

I HAVE the honor to transmit a report respecting roads and canals, prepared in obedience to the resolution of the Senate, of the 2d of March, 1807. It has been unavoidably delayed much later than was desirable, or had been expected. Although early steps had been taken for obtaining the necessary information, the most important documents were not received till long after the commencement of this session, some indeed, within the last ten days. To analyze the whole, to select, arrange and condense the most interesting facts, was also a work of some labor. Time has not permitted to present the report in a more satisfactory form : but the mass of facts, which has been collected, will, it is hoped, be of some public utility.

I have the honor to be,
    With great respect,
        Sir,
    Your most obedient servant,

ALBERT GALLATIN.

The Hon. GEORGE CLINTON,
    President of the Senate.

REPORT.

*The Secretary of the Treasury, in obedience to the re-
solution of the Senate of the 2d March, 1807, respectfully submits the following report on roads and
canals.*

THE general utility of artificial roads and canals, is at this time so universally admitted, as hardly to require any additional proofs. It is sufficiently evident that, whenever the annual expense of
transportation on a certain route in its natural state,
exceeds the interest on the capital employed in
improving the communication, and the annual expense of transportation (exclusively of the tolls,) by
the improved route; the difference is an annual additional income to the nation. Nor does in that case
the general result vary, although the tolls may not
have been fixed at a rate sufficient to pay to the undertakers the interest on the capital laid out. They indeed, when that happens, lose; but the community is
nevertheless benefited by the undertaking. The
general gain is not confined to the difference between
the expenses of the transportation of those articles
which had been formerly conveyed by that route,
but many which were brought to market by other
channels, will then find a new and more advantageous direction; and those which on account of their
distance or weight could not be transported in any
manner whatever, will acquire a value, and become
a clear addition to the national wealth. Those and
many other advantages have become so obvious, that
in countries possessed of a large capital, where pro-

perty is sufficiently secure to induce individuals to lay out that capital on permanent undertakings, and where a compact population creates an extensive commercial intercourse, within short distances, those improvements may often, in ordinary cases, be left to individual exertion, without any direct aid from government.

There are however some circumstances, which, whilst they render the facility of communications throughout the United States an object of primary importance, naturally check the application of private capital and enterprize, to improvements on a large scale.

The price of labor is not considered as a formidable obstacle, because whatever it may be, it equally affects the expense of transportation, which is saved by the improvement, and that of effecting the improvement itself. The want of practical knowledge is no longer felt : and the occasional influence of mistaken local interests, in sometimes thwarting or giving an improper direction to public improvements, arises from the nature of man, and is common to all countries. The great demand for capital in the United States, and the extent of territory compared with the population, are, it is believed, the true causes which prevent new undertakings, and render those already accomplished, less profitable than had been expected.

1. Notwithstanding the great increase of capital during the last fifteen years, the objects for which it is required continue to be more numerous, and its application is generally more profitable than in Europe. A small portion therefore is applied to objects which offer only the prospect of remote and moderate profit. And it also happens that a less sum being subscribed at first, than is actually requisite for completing the work, this proceeds slowly ; the capital applied remains unproductive for a much longer time than was necessary, and the interest

accruing during that period, becomes in fact an injurious addition to the real expense of the undertaking.

2. The present population of the United States, compared with the extent of territory over which it is spread, does not, except in the vicinity of the seaports, admit that extensive commercial intercourse within short distances, which, in England and some other countries, forms the principal support of artificial roads and canals. With a few exceptions, canals particularly, cannot in America be undertaken with a view solely to the intercourse between the two extremes of, and along the intermediate ground which they occupy. It is necessary, in order to be productive, that the canal should open a communication with a natural extensive navigation which will flow through that new channel. It follows that whenever that navigation requires to be improved, or when it might at some distance be connected by another canal to another navigation, the first canal will remain comparatively unproductive, until the other improvements are effected, until the other canal is also completed. Thus the intended canal between the Chesapeake and Delaware, will be deprived of the additional benefit arising from the intercourse between New York and the Chesapeake, until an inland navigation, shall have been opened between the Delaware and New York. Thus the expensive canals completed around the falls of Potomac, will become more and more productive in proportion to the improvement, first of the navigation of the upper branches of the river, and then of its communication with the western waters. Some works already executed are unprofitable, many more remain unattempted, because their ultimate productiveness depends on other improvements, too extensive or too distant to be embraced by the same individuals.

The general government can alone remove these obstacles.

With resources amply sufficient for the completion of every practicable improvement, it will always supply the capital wanted for any work which it may undertake, as fast as the work itself can progress, avoiding thereby the ruinous loss of interest on a dormant capital, and reducing the real expense to its lowest rate.

With these resources, and embracing the whole union, it will complete on any given line all the improvements, however distant, which may be necessary to render the whole productive, and eminently beneficial.

The early and efficient aid of the *federal* government is recommended by still more important considerations. The inconveniencies, complaints, and perhaps dangers, which may result from a vast extent of territory, can no otherwise be radically removed, or prevented, than by opening speedy and easy communications through all its parts. Good roads and canals, will shorten distances, facilitate commercial and personal intercourse, and unite by a still more intimate community of interests, the most remote quarters of the United States. No other single operation, within the power of government, can more effectually tend to strengthen and perpetuate that union, which secures external independence, domestic peace, and internal liberty.

With that view of the subject, the facts respecting canals, which have been collected in pursuance of the resolution of the Senate, have been arranged un-the following heads :—

1. Great canals, from north to south, along the Atlantic sea coast.

2. Communications between the Atlantic and western waters.

3. Communications between the Atlantic waters, and those of the great lakes, and river St. Lawrence.

4. Interior canals.

GREAT CANALS, ALONG THE ATLANTIC SEA COAST.

THE map of the United States will shew that they possess a tide-water inland navigation, secure from storms and enemies, and which, from Massachusetts to the southern extremity of Georgia, is principally, if not solely, interrupted by four necks of land.—These are the isthmus of Barnstable; that part of New Jersey, which extends from the Rariton to the Delaware; the peninsula between the Delaware and the Chesapeake; and that low and marshy tract which divides the Chesapeake from Albemarle sound. It is ascertained that a navigation for sea vessels, drawing eight feet of water, may be effected across the three last; and a canal is also believed to be practicable, not perhaps across the isthmus of Barnstable, but from the harbor of Boston to that of Rhode Island. The Massachusetts canal would be about 26, the New Jersey about 28, and each of the two southern about 22 miles in length, making altogether less than one hundred miles.

Should this great work, the expense of which, as will hereafter be shewn, is estimated at about three millions of dollars, be accomplished, a sea vessel entering the first canal in the harbor of Boston, would through the bay of Rhode Island, Long Island sound, and the harbor of New York, reach Brunswick on the Rariton; thence pass through the second canal to Trenton on the Delaware, down that river to Christiana, or New Castle, and through the third canal to Elk river, and the Chesapeake; whence sailing down that bay, and up Elizabeth river, it would, through the fourth canal, enter the Albemarle sound, and by Pamptico, Core and Bogue sounds, reach Beaufort and Swansborough, in North Carolina. From the last mentioned place, the inland navigation, through Stumpy and Toomer's sounds, is continued with a diminished draft of water, and by cutting two low and narrow necks, not exceeding three miles together, to Cape Fear river; and thence, by an open but short and direct run along the coast, is reached that chain of islands between which and the main, the inland navigation is continued to St. Mary's, along the coast of South Carolina, and Georgia. It is unnecessary to add any comments on the utility of the work, in peace or war, for the transportation of merchandize, or the conveyance of persons.

The several papers under the letter (A.) herewith transmitted, contain the information which has been received on those several intended communications. The substance will now be stated.

I. MASSACHUSETTS CANAL.

1. SANDWICH isthmus, between Barnstable bay on the north, and Buzzard's bay on the south, had first attracted the public attention. Surveys and levels were taken, for the purpose of ascertaining the practicability of opening a cross cut, to be supplied by the sea itself, from the mouth of Back river, in Buzzard's bay, to the mouth of Scusset river, in Barnstable bay.

The distance was found to exceed 7 miles; the elevation of the highest intermediate ground is forty feet above low water mark in Barnstable bay; the depth of water at the mouth of Back river, does not at low water, exceed 7 feet and a half; and the channel to that spot through Buzzard bay, is obstructed by shoals. The tide which rises but three feet and and a half in that bay, rises three hours and a half later, and more than eighteen feet in that of Barnstable. The shore on which that formidable tide would operate, is an open beach, without any harbor or shelter whatever. Independent of other obstacles, it was apprehended that the same natural causes, which had formed the isthmus, might fill the canal, or make a bar at its entrance; and the project seems to have been abandoned.

2. The ground was also examined between Barn-

stable harbor on the north, and Hyannus harbor on the south, at some distance east of Sandwich. The breadth of the peninsula does not exceed here four miles and a half, and there would be an harbor at each end of the canal. The same difference exists in the tides which rise 4 feet in Hyannus, and 16 feet in Barnstable harbor. The entrance of this is obstructed by shoals; but the great obstacle to a cross cut, is the elevation of the intermediate ground, estimated at 80 feet above tide water. Navigable ponds on that high ground might perhaps form part of a lock canal, and supply the remainder with water. But a canal frozen in winter, would not have effected the great object in view, which was to enable vessels from sea, to proceed in winter from Martha's Vineyard, to Boston, witho t sailing around Cape Cod. Although the difficulty of the navigation from Boston to Barnstable, diminishes the utility of this communication, as one of the great links in this line of inland navigation, it may be resorted to, should that which will be next mentioned, prove impracticable for sea vessels.

3. The attention of the legislature of Massachusetts, under whose authority the grounds at Sandwich and Barnstable, had been examined, has lately been turned to a direct communication between Weymouth landing, within the harbor of Boston, and Taunton river, which empties into the bay of Rhode Island. A favorable report has been made, during the last session, of which a copy has lately been obtained. The distance from tide water to tide water, is 26 miles by one route, and 23 1-4 miles by another. The highest intermediate ground, is 133 feet above tide water, but may be reduced ten feet, by digging to that depth, the length of a mile. Two ponds known by the names of Weymouth and Cranberry, the largest and least elevated of which covers five hundred acres, and is 14 feet higher than the summit of the proposed canal, will supply the upper locks with water by feeders, four miles long. Whether the quantity of water contained in the

ponds, and estimated equal to a daily supply of 450,000 cubic feet, will be sufficient for a sloop navigation; and whether any other ponds or streams may be brought in aid, does not seem to be fully ascertained. After descending twenty feet towards Weymouth, and seventy towards Taunton, an ample supply for the lower locks, will be derived from other large ponds, the principal of which are known by the names of Braintree and Nippinitic.

The expense may, on a supposition that the route is partly through a rocky soil, be estimated as follows:

Digging 26 miles, at $ 30,000 a mile, $ 780,000
Lockage 260 feet, at $ 1,250 a foot,   325,000
Feeders, purchase of land, &c.   145,000
                               1,250,000

II. New Jersey Canal.

A Company was incorporated some years ago, by the legislature of New Jersey, for opening a canal between the Rariton and the Delaware. Acting under the erroneous opinion that the navigation of small rivers might be improved and used as a canal, the company intended to have united, by a cross cut of one mile, the Assampink or Trenton Creek, with Stoney brook, a branch of Millstone river, and to have descended Trenton creek to the Delaware, and Stoney brook, and Millstone river, to the Rariton. The capital, which was inadequate, was not paid; but their survey of the intended route, has shewn the practicability of a canal for sea vessels, on a proper plan.

The distance from Brunswick to Trenton is 26 miles, and the only obstacle in the way is the " Sand hills," some distance west of Brunswick. These may, it is said, be avoided by a deviation which would not encrease the distance more than two miles; and they may at all events be perforated, as has been done by the turnpike company, who have opened a road on a straight line between the two towns, without having in any place an angle of ascent of more than three degrees.

The highest intermediate ground between Assampink and Stoney brook, is only fifty feet above tide water; and it is suggested that the summit level may be taken seven feet lower, cutting seven miles through a level meadow, between the confluence of the Assampink, and Shippetankin creeks, and Rowley's mill, near the confluence of Stoney brook and Millstone river.

An adequate supply of water will be drawn by short feeders, from Philip's springs, Trenton creek, Stoney brook, and Millstone river, all of which are more elevated than the route of the canal, the " Sand hills" excepted.

The depth of water at the two extremities of the canal, taken at low water, are   feet at Brunswick, and ten feet at Lamberton, one mile below Trenton.

The expenses may be estimated as followeth :

Digging 28 miles, at $ 20,000 per mile,	560,000
Lockage, 100 feet, (probably less) at $ 1250 per foot, - - - -	125,000
Feeders, purchase of land, and water rights, - - - - -	115,000
	$ 800,000

III. Delaware and Chesapeake Canal.

A Company incorporated by the states of Delaware and Maryland, for opening this canal, has commenced its operations, now suspended for want of funds.

The canal will commence at Welsh point on Elk river, an arm of the Chesapeake, and terminate at a distance of 22 miles, on Christiana creek, a branch of the Delaware. At low water the depth of water in Christiana is nine feet, and in Elk twelve feet, within one hundred feet from the shore. The tide rises four feet in both rivers. The canal might, without encreasing the distance, be conducted to New Castle on the Delaware itself, instead of ending at Christiana creek.

The highest intermediate ground, over which the canal will be carried on a level of 13 miles in length, is 74 feet above tide water, the descent being effected by nine locks on each side. The digging is generally easy : no expensive aqueducts or bridges, nor any other obstacles but those which have already been overcome in digging the feeder through a very rocky soil.

The supply of water drawn from Elk river, by a feeder six miles in length, already completed, which is itself a boat canal three and a half feet deep, united by a lock of ten feet lift with the main canal, is calculated to fill daily 144 locks ; a quantity sufficient on an average for the daily passage of twenty four vessels. A reservoir covering thirty, and which may be encreased to 150 acres, will supply occasional deficiencies : other reservoirs may be added, and Christiana and White Clay creeks may hereafter be brought in aid of Elk river, if the supply should prove too scanty for an encreased navigation.

The canal 26 feet wide at the bottom, and 50 at the top on the water line, being dug at the depth of 8 feet, is intended for vessels of forty to 70 tons, drawing 7 1-2 feet water : but the banks twenty feet wide for towing paths, and one of which may be converted into a turnpike road, being raised three feet above the level of the water, will, by encreasing the height of the lock gates one foot, admit a depth of nine feet of water in the canal ; at which depth it would perhaps be eligible to dig at once. The locks 80 feet long, 18 feet wide, and 8 (or 9) feet deep over the gate-sills, containing each 11,500 to 13,000 cubic feet of water, and with a lift of 8 to 9 feet each, will be constructed of hewn stone laid in tarras. Those dimensions both of the canal and locks, recommended by Mr. Latrobe, the engineer of the canal, may be adopted in all the other canals for sea vessels, on this line of communication.

The present annual carriage across the peninsula, which would be drawn through the canal, is estimated at forty two thousand tons, exclusively of passengers. This will be greatly encreased by the facility which the canal itself will afford to the commercial intercourse between the two bays, and to the conveyance of articles now carried through other channels, or too heavy for transportation, at the present expense of carriage. The coals wanted for Philadelphia, and which brought down from the sources of the Susquehanah and Potomac, but principally from the vicinity of Richmond, would naturally pass through the canal, have been alone estimated at more than one hundred thousand tons a year. The annual carriage of all articles may, in the present state of population, be fairly estimated at one hundred and fifty thousand tons, and the direct annual saving to the community at 300,000 dollars, being at the rate of 2 dollars a ton for the difference between land and water carriage across the peninsula, after paying the tolls. These, at the rate of fifty cents a ton, will give to the undertakers a revenue of 75,000 dollars, leaving, after a deduction of 10,000 dollars for annual repairs, and of 10,000 dollars more for attendance and contingencies, a nett income of 55,000 dollars.

The expenses of the whole work are estimated as followeth :

Digging 22 miles, at $ 20,000 a mile,	$ 440,000
18 locks, at 10,000 dollars each,	180,000
(The whole lockage being 148 feet, would at $ 1250 a foot, amount to 185,000 dollars.)	
Feeder, (nearly completed,) reservoirs, lock at the feeder, purchase of water rights and land, including a debt of dollars due by the company,	230,000
Dollars,	850,000

The interest on which sum, at 6 per cent. is 51,000 dollars.

The capital originally subscribed amounted to four hundred thousand dollars, divided into two thousand shares, of two hundred dollars each. One half of these has been forfeited after a small payment of five dollars on each share. One hundred thousand dollars paid by the other stockholders, have been expended in preparatory measures, in the purchase of water rights, and in digging the feeder, which was considered as the most difficult part of the work. Seven hundred and fifty thousand dollars are still wanted to complete the work; of which sum, one hundred thousand dollars is payable by the stockholders, and the deficiency of 650,000 dollars, must be drawn from other sources.

IV. CHESAPEAKE AND ALBEMARLE.

1. THE shortest communication between the Chesapeake and Albemarle sound, is from North landing at the head of the tide of North West river, which empties into Currituck inlet, the easternmost arm of Albemarle, to either Kempsville or Great Bridge, at the head of the tide of two different branches of the South branch of Elizabeth river, which passing by Norfolk, unites at Hampton roads, with James river, and the Chesapeake. The distance is stated at seven miles, and the levels said to be favorable. It is believed that the principal reason why this communication has not been attempted, is a bar in Currituck inlet, which does not admit the passage of vessels drawing five feet water.

2. A company incorporated by the states of Virginia and North Carolina, for opening a canal through the Dismal swamp, has made considerable progress in the work.

The canal extends 22 miles in length from Deep creek, a branch of the South branch of Elizabeth river, 7 miles above Norfolk, to Joyce's creek, a branch of Pasquotank river, a northern arm of Albemarle sound. Vessels drawing 8 to 9 feet water may ascend both creeks to each extremity of the canal.

The intervening ground along the eastern margin of the Dismal swamp, is almost level, the rise towards the middle not exceeding two feet above the two extremities, which are only 18 feet and 9 inches above tide water. The digging is very easy ; the only obstacles arise from the stumps and roots of trees, and are nearly overcome; and a single aqueduct or rather culvert over a small run emptying into the North West river is necessary.

The swamp itself supplies at the depth at which the canal is cut, the water which has heretofore been wanted ; and a sufficient supply may be drawn by a feeder of 3 miles and a half in length, cut through a perfect level from lake Drummond, a natural reservoir in the center of the swamp, of fifteen miles in circumference, and about six feet higher than the water in the canal.

The canal as cut by the company is 24 feet wide, and 6 feet deep, with one bank on the west side for a towing path, 18 feet broad. The whole digging, with the exception of two miles which must be deepened 3 feet, and of three quarters of a mile in another place not entirely finished, has been completed. The locks at the two extremities of the canal are not built; but two have been erected at some distance from each extremity ; probably in order to save some digging in the intervening space : they are made of square juniper logs, and have cost only three hundred dollars each.

The expense of digging has not exceeded 4,000 dollars a mile ; the whole capital expended, amounts to one hundred thousand dollars, of which the state of Virginia has furnished 17,500; and it is stated that the whole work may be completed in one year, and will not, including the locks and the payment of some debts contracted by the company, exceed 25,000 dollars. But the canal, which by the original act of incorporation was to be 32 feet wide, and 8 feet deep, can on its present plan be considered only as a local object, the principal utility of which consists in bringing to market the otherwise useless lumber of the swamp. The only boats which navigate it are flats, forty feet long, six feet wide, drawing two feet of water and carrying eight thousand shingles.

It must, in order to become a national object, be capable of receiving the vessels which navigate Albemarle sound, and for that purpose be restored to its first intended dimensions, or rather be widened and deepened, on the plan adopted for the Chesapeake and Delaware canal. The expense would be as followeth :

Digging, deepening to 8 feet, preserving
   the same level the whole way, and
   widening to a proper breadth, 22
   miles, at 8,000 dollars a mile, - $ 176,000
4 Stone locks at $ 10,000,   - -   40,000
Feeder to lake Drummond, aqueduct
   and contingencies,   -   -   -   34,000

                           $ 250,000

3. The last mentioned canal is in the most direct line of the communication through Albemarle to Pamtico sound, and the adjacent Southern sounds. It has been objected, that the navigation of Pasquotank river was intricate, and that it would be more advantageous to open a communication with Chowan river, which passing by Edenton, and then uniting with the Roanoke, forms Albemarle sound.

A company was incorporated for that purpose; but the capital was not filled, and no other operation performed, but surveying the ground. The intended canal on that route, would commence at Suffolk, on Nansemond river, which empties into James river, a few miles above, and west of the mouth of Elizabeth river; and passing along the western margin of the Dismal swamp, would reach at a computed distance of thirty miles, Gates' court house on Bennet's creek, a branch of Chowan river, which vessels drawing ten feet of water may ascend to that spot.

The highest intermediate ground is 28 feet above tide water and consequently higher than the surface of lake Drummond. But Bennet's creek and Curripeake swamp were considered as affording a sufficient supply of water. Should this prove adequate, the principal objection to this route will be, that the canal lands at Suffolk instead of Norfolk. This consideration, and the capital already expended on the canal from Elizabeth river to Pasquotank, seem to give a preference to this course. To which may be added, that if it be preferable to strike the waters of Chowan river, a lateral canal may be hereafter opened, along the southern margin of the Dismal swamp, from the southern extremity of the Elizabeth and Pasquotank canal, to Bennet's creek or Edenton. Whatever route may, after a critical examination of the ground, be thought the most eligible, the opening of this communication will be more easy and less expensive than either of the three northern canals.

The following table is a recapitulation of the distance to be cut on the whole line, and of the estimated expense.

CANALS.	DIRECTION.	Distance. Miles.	LOCKAGE Feet.	EXPENSE. Dollars.
Massachusetts,	Weymouth to Taunton,	26	260	1,250,000
New Jersey,	Brunswick to Trenton,	28	100	800,000
Delaware and Chesapeake,	Christiana to Elk,	22	148	750,000
Chesapeake & Albemarle,	Eliz. riv. to Pasquotank	22	40	250,000
	Total.	98	548	3,050,000

COMMUNICATIONS BETWEEN THE AT
LANTIC AND WESTERN WATERS.

THE Apalachian mountains, to use an ancient generic denomination, extend in a direction west of south, from the 42d to the 34th degree of north latitude, approaching the sea, and even washed by the tide in the state of New York, and thence in their southerly course, gradually receding from the sea shore. Viewed as a whole, their breadth may be estimated at 110 miles, and they consist of a succession of parallel ridges, following nearly the direction of the sea coast, irregularly intersected by rivers, and divided by narrow vallies. The ridge, which divides the Atlantic rivers from the western waters, generally known by the name of Allegheny, preserves throughout a nearly equal distance of 250 miles from the Atlantic ocean, and a nearly uniform elevation of 3,000 feet above the level of the sea.

Those mountains may, however, be perhaps considered as consisting of two principal chains : between these lies the fertile lime-stone valley, which, although occasionally interrupted by transversal ridges, and in one place, by the dividing or Allegheny ridge, may be traced from Newburgh and Esopus, on the Hudson river, to Knoxville on the Tennessee.

The eastern and narrowest chain is the Blue Ridge of Virginia, which in its north east course traverses under various names, the states of Maryland, Pennsylvania, and New Jersey, forms the high lands broken at West point by the tide of the Hudson, and then uniting with the Green mountains, assumes a northerly direction, and divides the waters of the Hudson, and of lake Champlain, from those of Connecticut river. On the borders of Virginia and North Carolina, the Blue Ridge is united by an inferior mountain, with the great western chain, and thence to its southern extremity, becomes the principal or dividing mountain, discharging eastwardly the rivers Roanoke, Pedee, Santee, and Savannah, into the Atlantic ocean; southwardly the Chatahouchee, and the Alabama into the gulph of Mexico, and westwardly the New river and the Tennessee. The New river, taking a northwardly course, breaks through all the ridges of the great western chain, and at a short distance beyond it, unites under the name of Kanhawa, with the Ohio. The Tennessee pursues, at first, a south west direction between the two chains, until having reached, and in a westwardly course turned the southern extremity of the great western chain, it assumes a northwardly direction, and joins its waters with those of the Ohio, a few miles above the confluence of that river with the Mississippi.

The western chain, much broader, and generally more elevated, is known under the names of Cumberland and Gauley mountains, from its southern extremity, near the great bend of the Tennessee river, until it becomes in Virginia, the principal or dividing mountain. Thence in its northerly course, towards the state of New York, it discharges westwardly the Green Briar river, which, by its junction with the New river, forms the Kanhawa, and the rivers Monongahela and Allegheny, which, from their confluence at Pittsburgh, assume the name of Ohio. Eastwardly it pours into the Atlantic ocean, James river, the Potomac, and the Susquehannah. From the northernmost and less elevated spurs of the chain, the Genessee flows into the lake Ontario; and in that quarter the northerly branches of the Susquehanna seem to take their source, from amongst inferior ridges, and in their course to the Chesapeake, to break through all the mountains. From the Susquehannah, the principal chain assumes a more eastwardly direction, and washed on the north by the lateral valley of the river Mowhawk, whilst it gives rise southwardly to the Delaware, it terminates under the name of Catskill mountain, in view of the tide water of the Hudson.

This description has been introduced for the double purpose of pointing out all the rivers which can afford the means of communication, and of shewing the impracticability, in the present state of science, of effecting a canal navigation across the mountains.

The most elevated lock canal of which a correct description has been given, is that of Languedoc, and the highest ground over which it is carried, is only six hundred feet above the sea. It is not believed that any canal has been undertaken, or at least completed in England, of an elevation exceeding 430 feet above the waters united by it. The Allegheny mountain is generally, and from observations made in several places, about 3,000 feet above the level of the sea. The precise height of the dividing ridge was ascertained by the commissioners, who laid out the United States road from Cumberland on the Potomac to Brownsville on the Monongahela, at 2260 above the first, and at 2150 feet above the last river. Cumberland, from the levels taken by the Potomac company, is itself 735 feet above tide water. Although some more advantageous and less elevated places may be found, particularly amongst the ridges which divide some of the upper branches of the Susquehannah from the corresponding streams emptying into the river Allegheny, there is none which is not of an elevation much beyond what has ever been overcome by canals in any other country. The impracticability arises from the principle of lock navigation, which in order to effect the ascent, requires a greater supply of water in proportion to the height to be ascended, whilst the supply of water becomes less in the same proportion. Nor does the chain of mountains through the whole extent, where it divides the Atlantic from the western rivers, afford a single pond, lake or natural reservoir. It may be added as a general feature of American geography, that except in the swamps along the southern sea coast, no lake is to be found in the United States, south of 41 degrees north latitude; and that almost every river, north of 42 degrees, issues from a lake or pond.

The works necessary in order to facilitate the communications from the sea ports across the mountains to the western waters, must therefore consist either of artificial roads extending the whole way from tide water, to the nearest and most convenient navigable western waters; or of improvements in the navigation of the leading Atlantic rivers, to the highest practicable points, connected by artificial roads across the mountains, with the nearest points from which a permanent navigation can be relied on, down the western rivers.

The principal considerations in selecting proper directions for those communications, are, the distance from the navigable western waters, both to tide water, and to the nearest navigable Atlantic river, and the extent of navigation, either natural or susceptible of improvement, which may be afforded by the rivers. Distance alone is mentioned, so far as relates to roads, because the mountains however insuperable for canals, offer no important impediment to land communications. So far from being an insurmountable barrier to commercial intercourse, between the two great sections of the union, it is now ascertained that those mountains may almost in every direction be crossed by artificial roads, as permanent, as easy, and less expensive, than similar works in the lower country. For congress having, contrary to current opinion, directed that the road from Cumberland to Brownsville should be laid out so that its ascent should not in any place exceed an angle of five degrees with the horizon; no difficulty has been experienced in effecting the object without cutting through hills, and although the road thus laid out, be in a distance of 72 miles, two or three miles shorter than that heretofore in use.

Although the distance from the sea to the principal dividing mountain through its whole length, between the western sources of the Susquehannah, and

those of the Savannah, be nearly the same, yet the
Atlantic bays, penetrating the coast at different
depths, and in different directions, the distances from
the sea ports to the nearest western navigable waters, vary considerably. Taken in straight lines
from each port to the nearest branch, beyond all the
mountains, of each of the four great western rivers,
they may be stated as follows :

From Philadelphia to the confluence of Conemaugh and Loyalhannon,	*Miles*
branches of the *Allegheny*, - - -	220
From the City of Washington to the con- fluence of the rivers *Monongahela* and Cheat, - - - - -	150
From Richmond to Morris's on the *Kanhawa*, below all the falls of that river, - - - - - -	210
From Savannah or Charleston to any navigable branch of *Tennessee*, the dis- tance exceeds - - - -	800

The distance from the same western points, to the
upper navigation of the corresponding Atlantic rivers,
cannot be stated with precision, as the upper points to
which the navigation of those rivers may be improved,
is not yet ascertained. The shortest portage between
the waters of the Potomac, and those of the Monongahela, in their natural state, from West Port on the
Potomac, to Cheat river below the falls, is about
fifty miles in a straight line. But in order to secure
a tolerable navigation, particularly on the Potomac,
the route from Cumberland to Brownsville, (Red
Stone old fort) has been preferred, and the distance
by the road lately laid out is 72 miles. The portage
between the North fork of the Juniata, a branch of
the Susquehanna, and the corresponding waters of
the river Allegheny, is somewhat shorter. That between Pattonborough, on James river, and the falls
of the Kanhawa, exceeds one hundred miles.

The most prominent, though not perhaps the most
insuperable obstacle in the navigation of the Atlantic

rivers, consists in their lower falls, which are ascribed to a presumed continuous granite ridge, rising about 130 feet above tide water. That ridge, from New York to James river inclusively, arrests the ascent of the tide ; the falls of every river within that space being precisely at the head of the tide. Pursuing thence southwardly a direction nearly parallel to the mountains, it recedes from the sea, leaving in each southern river, an extent of good navigation between the tide and the falls. Other falls of less magnitude are found at the gaps of the Blue Ridge, through which the rivers have forced their passage. Higher up the rapidity of the northern rivers, which penetrate through the inferior ridges of the great western chain, encreases as they approach, the dividing or Allegheny mountain; and their sources being nearly at the same elevation, their rapidity encreases in proportion to the shortness of their course. For that reason the navigation of the Susquehannah above the Blue Ridge is better than that of the Potomac, which affords as has been stated, the shortest communcation from tide water to the nearest western river. The levels of the last mentioned river having been taken by the Potomac company, the general result is annexed, as giving a more correct idea of the navigation of the Atlantic rivers, than could be conveyed in any other manner.

	DISTANCE. Miles.	FALL. Feet.	RATE OF FALL. Feet pr. mile.
From the mouth of Savage river, down to Cumberland,	31	445	14 1-2
Thence to the Blue Ridge,	130 1-2	490	4
Harper's Ferry, or Shenandoe Falls,	5 1-2	43	
Thence to Great Falls,	40	39	1
Great and Little Falls, to tide water,	12	143	
Total,	219	1,160	

The papers marked (C.) contain the information which h.s been collected respecting the works executed or contemplated on the great rivers already enumerated. It has not been understood that any improvements of importance had been yet attempted on the Savannah and Pedee, nor on any of the tributary streams of the Ohio; and the communications received under this head, relate only to the Santee, Roanoke, James river, Potomac, Susquehannah, and Ohio.

I. SANTEE.

THE Santee or Catawba, is said to be occasionally navigable for near 300 miles, as high up as Morgantown, in North Carolina. Two companies have been incorporated by that state, and that of South Carolina, for the purpose of improving its navigation The lower falls are above Camden and not far from the arsenal of the United States, at Mount Rock. A canal had been commenced there, but either from want of success in the commencement, or from want of funds, the work appears to be suspended. The market for the produce brought down that river is Charleston; and the river boats were obliged at the mouth of the river to enter the sea, and to reach that port by a navigation along the sea shore, for which they were not calculated. To remedy that inconvenience, and to insure a permanent navigation, a canal has been opened by another company, uniting the Santee with Cooper river, which empties into the harbor of Charleston.

The distance between the points united, is 22 miles: the highest intervening ground was 52 feet above Santee, and 85 feet above the river Cooper; but it has been reduced 17 feet by digging; the descent to Santee being 35 feet, effected by four locks, and that to Cooper 68 feet, effected by nine locks.

The principal supply of water is afforded by

springs arising from the marshy ground at the bottom of the canal, and by several drains which collect and bring from an adjacent swamp the sources of the river Cooper. The quantity is said to be seldom deficient; yet a steam engine has been contemplated as perhaps necessary in order to raise from the Santee an adequate supply.

The canal was carried over some small streams by means of aqueducts; inconsiderable ravines have been filled, and the ground was dug in some places to the depth of sixteen feet, in order to preserve the level. But it appears that the roots of trees were the greatest obstacle encountered in digging the canal. Its breadth is 20 feet at the bottom, and 35 feet at top: the depth of water is 4 feet; and it admits boats of 20 tons. The locks made of brick, faced with marble, are 60 feet long, and 10 feet wide.

The capital expended is stated at 650,667 dollars, including sixty negroes and some tracts of land belonging to the company. The canal has been completed six years; the annual tolls had never exceeded 13,000 dollars before the year 1807, and the annual expenses are stated at 7,000 dollars. The want of success in this undertaking, which though completed is very unprofitable, may be ascribed to several causes. The expense compared with the work is much greater than might have been expected, and probably than was necessary. The locks are too small for large boats, which are therefore obliged to pursue the former route down the Santee, and by sea to Charleston; and want of water is alledged as a sufficient reason for the size of the locks. But a canal in that situation cannot in America be profitable unless the navigation of the main river with which it communicates, is rendered safe and permanent; and whenever that of the Santee itself shall have been improved, the utility and profits of the canal will be considerably encreased.

II. The Lower or Great Falls of Roanoke

Consist in a succession of rapids, which in a distance of fifteen miles have a fall of ninety three feet. This obstruction is such that almost all the tobacco of that river is transported by land to Petersburgh, on the Appomatox branch of James river. A canal has been contemplated from the upper end of the falls to Murfreesborough, situated on the tide water of a branch of Chowan river, 25 miles above the mouth of Bennet's creek, which has been before mentioned as one of the lines of communication between Albemarle sound and the Chesapeake. The level is said to be favorable, without any obstructions or vallies in the way. The distance is 38 miles, and the expense of a small canal for boats, drawing 2 feet and a half of water, may be estimated as followeth:

Digging 38 miles, at $ 6000 a mile, -	$ 228,000
Lockage 93 feet, at $ 800 a foot, - -	74,400
Feeder, land, &c. - - -	47,600
Dollars,	350,000

The capital for this canal has never been subscribed, and it has been suggested that it would be practicable to open one to Petersburgh. It is not believed that any hills intervene in that course; and the greatest obstacle will be found in crossing the branches of Chowan river.

III. James River.

A Company incorporated by the state of Virginia, for the improvement of the navigation of the river generally, has removed some obstructions in the upper part of the river, and is bound by the charter to render it so far navigable that there may never be less than 12 inches of water over any of the shoals or rapids, from the upper end of the lower or great falls to Pattonborough, a distance of 220 miles. The natural navigation of the river through that extent is considered as better than that of any other Atlantic river above the falls.

A communication has been opened by the company from Westham, at the upper end of the great falls, to Shockoe hill in the city of Richmond, in the following manner: The water is drawn at Westham from the river into a canal 200 yards in length, at the end of which, boats descending 34 feet through three locks re-enter the river, and after using its natural navigation three miles, are brought by a canal 3 miles and a half in length to a bason on Shockoe hill, where the navigation terminates.

That bason is about 80 feet above tide water, and one mile and a half from Rockets, the port of Richmond. The whole fall from the upper end of the canal at Westham to the bason, may be stated at 48 feet, and the distance at six miles and a half. The canal is 25 feet wide, and admits boats of eight tons drawing three feet of water. The locks 80 feet long, and 16 feet wide, are of solid masonry; but the cement is defective. Three aqueducts have been thrown across valleys intervening in the course of the canal; and some difficult digging was necessary on the side of hills, and through ledges of rocks.

The canal, according to the charter, was intended to have been brought down to tide water. The performance of that condition is now suspended by an act of the legislatnre of Virginia, and there seems to be a considerable diversity of opinion on that subject. In a national point of view, the plan which will at the least expense put coals on board vessels lying at Rockets, deserves the preference. For coal is in no other part of the United States found in abundance in the vicinity of tide water. At present the expense of transportation by the canal is already reduced to one third of the land carriage.

The original capital of the company amounted to 140,000 dollars, of which the state of Virginia owns fifty thousand; and 91,000 dollars arising from the proceeds of tolls, had before the 1st January, 1805, been applied to the work, making together an expenditure of 231,000 dollars. The annual tolls raised on fourteen thousand tons of country produce, and on two thousand coal boats, have amounted to 16,750 dollars : and the annual repairs and expenses are estimated at 5000 dollars. But as the company draw also a revenue from the rent of water, applied to mills and other water works erected along the canal, they have been able in some years to make dividends of 16,800 dollars, being at the rate of 12 per cent. on the original capital, but of only about 7 per cent. if calculated on the sum of 244,000 dollars, the amount of capital expended, and interest accrued before any dividend was made.

IV. Potomac.

The company incorporated by the states of Maryland and Virginia, for improving the navigation of that river, has executed the following works.

1. At a distance of 12 miles above the head of the tide, which ascends about 3 miles above the city of Washington, the river is 143 feet higher than tide water. At that place designated by the name of *Great falls*, the boats passing through a canal one mile in length, six feet deep, and twenty five feet wide, descend 76 feet by five locks, 100 feet long, and 12 feet wide each, and re-entering the river, follow its natural bed, eight miles and a half. Another canal of the same dimensions, and two miles and a half in length, brings them then through three locks and by a descent of 37 feet to tide water. This last fall is distinguished by the name of *Little falls*. The two lower locks of the Great falls, excavated out of the solid rock, have each a lift of 18 feet : the three upper locks of solid masonary are of unequal height, and have together a lift of forty feet. The three locks of the Little falls, are each one hundred feet in length and eighteen feet wide. That breadth is unnecessary, and consumes two much water, a de-

fect which will be remedied, when stone locks will be substituted to those now in use, which being of wood, will soon be decayed.

Three other canals without locks have been opened around three distinct falls: the principal at the Shenandoe falls below Harper's ferry, and at the place where the Potomac breaks through the Blue Ridge, is one mile in length around a fall of fifteen feet. Between this and the Great falls another canal three quarters of a mile in length, is opened around the Seneca falls. The third, fifty yards in length, has been cut around Houre's falls, five miles above the Shenandoe falls. Above this place, the navigation has been improved by deepening occasionally the channel, raising the water in shallow places by small dams, and opening sluices along the shore. It is believed that by multiplying the number of those low dams, by throwing the channel along the shore, and when necessary opening canals with or without locks around the principal rapids, the navigation may be improved, perhaps as high up as Cumberland, 188 miles above tide water, to such a degree as to render the river passable for boats the greater part of the year. And if this be found practicable on the Potomac, which is the most rapid of the great Atlantic rivers, the same improvements may with greater facility be effected on any of the others. It will be indispensable, in order to attain that object on the Potomac, that additional canals with locks, should be opened at the Shenandoe or Blue Ridge falls, which as has already been stated, fall 43 feet, in the distance of five miles.

2. The Shenandoe, a river nearly as large as the Potomac itself, after a course of 250 miles through the Great Lime-stone valley, unites its waters with those of the Potomac at Harper's ferry, just above the Blue Ridge. From Port Republic till within eight miles of the Potomac, a distance of near 200 miles, it affords a good navigation, the fall of the river being at the rate of less than two feet a mile. In the

last eight miles it falls eighty feet, and was impassable before the improvements completed last year by the Potomac company. Six different canals, 20 feet wide, four feet and a half deep, and extending altogether 2400 yards, have been opened round the most difficult falls. Through those, and five stone locks, 100 feet long and 12 feet wide each, and effecting together a descent of near fifty feet, the communication is now opened, and will render the undertaking much more productive than heretofore. The water in all those canals and locks, as well as in those executed on the Potomac, is uniformly supplied by the river itself.

The capital originally subscribed amounted to 311,560 dollars, divided into 701 shares; of which the state of Maryland owns 220, and the state of Virginia seventy. The total amount expended, including an additional payment received from late subscribers, 38,000 dollars arising from tolls, which have been applied to the work, and a debt of about 67,000 dollars contracted by the company, amounts to 444,652 dollars. The annual tolls raised on eight thousand tons of sundry articles, valued at more than half a million of dollars, have not before the opening of the Shenandoe, exceeded 15,000 dollars; and the annual expenses and repairs are stated at 5,000 dollars.

One hundred shares of £. 145 sterling each, remain open for subscription.

V. SUSQUEHANNAH.

THIS river has no perpendicular or altogether impassable falls: but from the head of the tide up to the Pennsylvania line, a distance of ten miles, the navigation is impeded by a succession of dangerous rapids; and these, though occasionally separated by sheets of smooth water, continue 40 miles higher up, at least as far as Columbia; the whole fall from this place, to the head of the tide, being estimated at about

140 feet. The navigation through that distance, at all times dangerous, is practicable only during the high freshets, when rafts and flat bottomed boats, 80 feet long and 17 feet wide, may descend from the several widely extended upper branches of the river. Less dangerous falls are found at the place where it breaks through the Blue Ridge; above which the natural navigation from Middletown upwards, whether up the Juniata, the West branch, or the East branch, is much better than that of the Potomac, and has been improved in several places at the expense of the state of Pennsylvania. A canal one mile long, and 4 feet deep, with two brick locks, has also been opened around the Conewago falls, in the gap of the Blue Ridge, fourteen thousand dollars having been paid for that object by the same state. Its entrance is difficult, and it is used for water works, being free for navigation, though private property. From Columbia down to the Maryland line, considerable improvements in the bed of the river have also been made at the expense of the two states, and the descending navigation has on the whole been improved: but few boats ever attempt to ascend. Nor is it believed that the natural advantages of the most considerable Atlantic river will ever be fully enjoyed, until a canal shall have been opened the whole way from Columbia, either to tide water, or to the Delaware and Chesapeake canal.

A company incorporated by the state of Maryland, for opening a canal around the falls, in that part of the river which extends from the Pennsylvania line, to tide water, has completed that part of the work, the utility of which is but very partially felt, whilst the bed of the river remains the only communication from its upper extremity up to Columbia.

The canal, 30 feet wide, 3 feet deep, and admitting boats of 20 tons, is nine miles in length, with a fall of 59 feet. The descent is effected by eight stone locks, each of which is 100 feet in length, and 12 feet wide. The water is supplied by the river itself; and in order to cross the rivers Conawingo and Octorara, these, by means of dams, have been raised ten and twelve feet to the level of the canal.

Its defects consist in 'the want of sufficient breadth of the locks, which do not admit the rafts and wide flat bottom boats, generally used in bringing down the country produce, and in want of water at the lower end of the canal. This last defect may be remedied by extending the canal 700 yards lower down along the edge of the river ; and it is probable, that as timber will become more scarce and valuable in the upper branches of the Susquehannah, boats of a different construction will be used. In the mean while, the annual tolls have not yet amounted to one thousand, whilst the annual expenses are stated at twelve hundred dollars, and the capital expended at 250,000 dollars.

The attempts made to open a communication from Middletown, in the Lime stone valley, to Philadelphia, partly by canals, and partly by means of the Skuylkill, will be noticed under the head of "Interior Canals."

VI. Ohio.

The navigation of the Kanhawa, and of the eastern branches of the Tennessee, Monongahela, and Allegheny, in their course through the mountains, may at a future period be improved. But from the foot of the mountains, all those rivers, and particularly the Ohio, flow with a much gentler current than the Atlantic rivers : a circumstance easily accounted for, when it is recollected that Brownsville on the Monongahela, and at a distance of two thousand miles by water from the sea, is only 115 feet more elevated than Cumberland on the Potomac ; whilst this river with all its meanders, reaches tide water, within less than two hundred miles. All those rivers at the annual melting of the snows rise to the height of more than forty feet, affording from the upper points to which they are navigable, a safe navigation to the sea for any ship that can pass over the bar at the mouth of the Mississippi. As early as the year 1793, a schooner built on the Monongahela, between Brownsville and Pittsburgh, reached New Orleans by that extraordinary inland navigation, and arrived safely at Philadelphia. This first essay, stimulated the spirit of enterprize so conspicuous in the American character; and numerous vessels from one hundred to three hundred and fifty tons burthen are now annually built at several ship yards on the Ohio, even as high up as Pittsburgh, and bringing down to New Orleans the produce of the upper country consumed there, carry to Europe, and to the Atlantic ports of the United States, the sugar, the cotton, and the tobacco of Louisiana, and of the states of Tennessee and Kentucky.

That branch of national industry gives value to the immense forests of the Ohio and of its numerous branches, will soon make a considerable and perhaps necessary accession to the shipping of the United States, and has a tendency to diminish the price of freights from New Orleans to the other American and to foreign ports. The importance of this last consideration will be duly felt, if the magnitude of the exports, of which New Orleans is destined to be the emporium, be contrasted with the probable amount of its importations. For such are the labor, time and expense necessary to ascend the rapid stream of the Mississippi; and the nature of its banks annually overflowed on a breadth of several miles, precludes the possibility of towing paths; that whilst the greater part of the produce of the immense country watered by that river and its tributary streams, must necessarily be exported through its channel, the importations of a considerable portion of that country will continue to be supplied from the Atlantic sea ports, by water and land communications, susceptible of considerable improvement. And thus unless another outlet be found for a portion of the

exports, or unless the upper country can supply vessels, those exports must necessarily pay a double
freight.

The only impediments to that navigation are, on
the Tennessee, "the Muscle shoals," of which no
particular account has been received; and, on the
Ohio, the falls of Louisville. Ordinary boats can
with difficulty pass these in summer, and the navigation is even during the freshets, dangerous for the
large vessels. The attention of the legislature of
Kentucky, and of the inhabitants of the western
country generally, has therefore been particularly
drawn to the opening of a canal at that place. A company has been lately incorporated by the state of Kentucky for that purpose, with a capital which may
amount to 500,000 dollars, but a small portion of
which has yet been subscribed. The expense however is estimated at a sum less than the nominal capital.

The proposed canal would be near two miles in
length, and must be dug, in some places to a depth
of 27, but generally of about 16 feet; the breadth at
the bottom being 20 feet with the necessary slope,
would make it generally 68 feet wide at top, and in
particular places not less than one hundred. The fall
at low water is about 22 feet, and would require three
locks of dimensions sufficient to pass ships of 400
tons, and drawing 14 feet of water. The greatest
expense will be that of digging and removing the
earth, which may be estimated at 400,000 cubic
yards, and according to the representation made of
the nature of the ground, will not probably cost more
than 200,000 dollars. To this may be added 100,000
dollars for the locks and other necessary works, making altogether three hundred thousand dollars. The
greatest difficulty seems to be the protection of the
locks and canals against the rise of the river, which
sometimes overflows the whole ground through
which the canal must be opened.

THE expense of the improvements suggested in the communications between the Atlantic and western waters, may be stated as followeth:

1st. Four artificial roads from the four great western rivers, the Allegheny, Monongahela, Kanhawa, and Tennessee, to the nearest corresponding Atlantic rivers, the Susquehannah or Juniata, the Potomac, James river, and either the Santee or Savannah, leaving to the several states the continuation of those roads eastwardly to the nearest sea ports. Those roads should unite on each river, points from which a permanent and safe navigation downwards could, except during the driest seasons, be relied on, and will therefore on each route be estimated at one hundred miles, making altogether 400 miles, which at 7000 dollars a mile, the materials being generally on the spot, would cost -   -   - $ 2,800,000

2dly. The improvement of the navigation of the four Atlantic rivers from tide water to the highest practicable point, effected principally by canals around the falls wherever practicable, and by locks whenever necessary. The most expensive of these would be the proposed canal from Columbia on the Susquehanah, either to tide water, or to the Delaware & Chesapeake canal. And considering how much has been effected already, and may still be done on the other rivers by the several incorporated companies, it is believed that every useful improvement might be completed by a public expenditure not exceeding $ 1,500,000

3dly. The canal at the falls of Ohio, estimated at -   -   -   - $ 300,000

Making altogether, -   - $ 4,600,000

Although a canal navigation, uniting the Atlantic and western waters in a direct course across the mountains appears impracticable, yet those mountains may be turned either on the north by means of the Mohawk valley and of lake Ontario, or on the south through Georgia, and the Mississippi territory. The first communication will be noticed under the head of "the river St. Laurence and great lakes." Of the second it will be sufficient to observe, that the country lying between the sources of the rivers Chatahouchee and Mobile, and the gulph of Mexico, is an inclined plane, regularly descending towards the sea, and that by following the proper levels, it presents no natural obstacle to the opening of a canal, fed by the waters of the two last mentioned rivers, and extending from the tide water on the coast of Georgia, to the Mississippi. The distance in a direct line is about 550 miles, and to be overcome, requires only time, perseverance and labor. When it is recollected that such an undertaking would discharge the Mississippi into the Atlantic, the remarks already made on the trade of that river, and other obvious considerations, will sufficiently point out its immence importance. Nor should the plan, on account of its magnitude, be thought chimerical; for the elevation and other natural obstacles of intervening ground, or want of a sufficient suply of water, and not distance, are the only insuperable impediments to an artificial navigation.

This work, which is presented not as an immediate but as a distant object, worthy of consideration, would probably require ten millions of dollars, and thirty years for its completion. The annual sales of the public lands in the Mississippi territory, which are estimated at fifty millions of acres, would after paying the debt due to the state of Georgia, afford sufficient funds ; and the encreased value of the residue, would alone more than compensate the expense.

It is proper to add, that an inland navigation, even for open boats, already exists from New Orleans by the canal Carondelet, to the lake Pontchartrain, thence between the coast and the adjacent islands to

the bay of Mobile, and up its two pri'
Alibama, and the Tombigbee to th'
within the acknowledged boundaries
States. The current of these two rivers be
less rapid than that of the Mississippi, they have
been contemplated, particularly the Tombigbee, a.
affording a better communication to the ascending
or returning trade from New Orleans to the waters
of the Tennessee, from which they are separated by
short portages.

COMMUNICATIONS BETWEEN THE AT-
LANTIC RIVERS,

AND THE

RIVER ST. LAURENCE AND GREAT LAKES.

Vessels ascend the river St. Laurence from
the sea to Montreal. The river Sorel discharges at
some distance below that town the waters of lake
George and lake Champlain, which penetrate southwardly within the United States. From Montreal to
lake Ontario, the ascent of the river St. Laurence is
estimated at about 200 feet. From the eastern extremity of lake Ontario, an inland navigation for vessels of more than 100 tons burthen, is continued
more than one thousand miles, through lakes Erie,
St. Clair, and Huron, to the western and southern
extremities of lake Michigan, without any other in-
terruption than that of the falls and rapids of Niagara,
between lake Erie and lake Ontario. The descent
from fort Schlosser to Devil's hole, a distance of
four miles, which includes the perpendicular falls of
Niagara, has by correct measurement been ascertained at 375 feet. The whole fall from lake Erie
to lake Ontario, is estimated at 450 feet, making the
elevation of lake Erie above tide water, six hundred
and fifty feet.

Lake Superior, the largest of those inland seas, communicates with the northern extremity of lake Huron, by the river and rapids of St. Mary's. The fall of these is not ascertained: but it is said that a small canal has been opened around the most difficult part, by the North West Fur company.

Five of the Atlantic rivers approach the waters of the St. Laurence; viz. The Penobscot, Kennebeck, Connecticut, the North, or Hudson river, and the Tioga branch of the Susquehannah. This last river will afford a useful communication with the rivers Seneca, and Genessee, which empty into lake Ontario. The length of the portage has not been precisely stated; and the general navigation of the Susquehannah has already been noticed. It may however be observed, that it is the only Atlantic river whose sources approach both the western waters, and those of the St. Laurence.

The three eastern rivers, afford convenient communications with the province of Lower Canada, but not with that extensive inland navigation, which penetrates through the United States, within two hundred miles of the Mississippi. No statement has been received of any improvement having yet been made on the Penobscot, or Kennebeck; and a very imperfect account has been obtained of some short canals opened around the several falls of the river Connecticut. One at Bellows' falls, in the state of Vermont, has been particularly mentioned, and is the highest improvement on the river.

What is called the North river, is a narrow and long bay, which in its northwardly course from the harbor of New York, breaks through, or turns all the mountains, affording a tide navigation for vessels of 80 tons to Albany and Troy, 160 miles above New York. This peculiarity distinguishes the North river from all the other bays and rivers of the United States. The tide in no other ascends higher than the granite ridge, or comes within thirty miles of the Blue Ridge, or eastern chain of mountains.

In the North river, it breaks through the Blue Ridge at West Point, and ascends above the eastern termination of the Catskill, or great western chain.

A few miles above Troy, and the head of the tide, the Hudson from the north, and the Mohawk from the west, unite their waters, and form the North river. The Hudson in its course upwards, approaches the waters of lake Champlain, and the Mohawk, those of lake Ontario.

I. Hudson and Champlain, or Northern Navigation.

A Company was incorporated several years ago by the state of New York, for the purpose of opening this communication, and a survey taken by Mr. Weston, a copy of which has not yet been obtained. From collateral information, it appears that it was proposed to open a canal 12 miles long, with a lockage of 106 feet, from Waterford, at the confluence of the Hudson and Mohawk, to the upper end of the great falls of Stillwater. This was considered as the most difficult part of the whole route, and the expense estimated at 275,000 dollars. Another canal and lock would be necessary around the falls of fort Miller: but the remainder of the navigation up the Hudson to fort Edward, does not require any material improvement.

At some distance above fort Edward, it was intended to connect by a canal and locks, the Hudson with the *North* Wood creek, at fort Ann. The navigation down the creek to Skeensborough is used, but requires to be improved. At this place, where falls render another canal necessary, North Wood creek empties into the south bay of lake Champlain; and thence is a natural sloop navigation through the whole extent of the lake. The expense of the works from fort Edward to Skeensborough, had been estimated at 200,000 dollars.

The funds of the company were insufficient, and

have, it is said, been expended without much permanent utility at Stillwater and Skeensborough.

The distance in a straight line from Waterford to Skeensborough is fifty miles; and the expense of opening a permanent boat navigation on a proper plan through the whole line, is from imperfect materials estimated at about 800,000 dollars. This communication would divert to a port of the United States the trade of one half of the state of Vermont, a id of a part of that of New York, which is now principally carried through the channel of the St. Laurence, and of the province of Canada.

II. Mohawk and Ontario, or Western Navigation.

A Company incorporated by the state of New York, for the improvement of this navigation, has made considerable progress, and an accurate survey having been taken of the distances and levels of the greater part of the route, the result will in the first place be stated.

	DIST. Miles.	FALL. Feet.
From the tide water at Troy to Lansing mills on the Mohawk, is found the greatest impediment to the navigation of that river, consisting of the Cohos falls, which are 70 feet perpendicular, and of a succession of other falls, which continue to the north river,	4 2-3	140
From Lansing mills up the Mohawk to Schenectady, the height of the river at the time when the survey was taken, prevented Mr. Weston from correctly ascertaining the levels. The fall for that distance is therefore estimated at	12 1-3	28 1-4
Carried forward,	17	168 1-4

	DIST. *Miles.*	FALL. *Feet.*
Brought forward,	17	168 1-4
From Schenectady to the Little falls, - - - -	57 1-2	110 1-2
The Little falls, which before the improvements made by the company, interrupted altogether the navigation, - - - -	3-4	42
From the little falls to fort Stanwix, now Rome, - -	48	59 1-2
This is the head of the navigation, and the summit level between it and West Wood creek, a branch of Lake Ontario, is 9 feet 3-4 above that part of the river Mohawk, where the navigation ceases, - - - - -	1 3-4	9 3-4
	125	390

The whole course of the Mohawk is therefore 125 miles in length, and the fall through that distance from the summit level to tide water is 390 feet.

At the distance of one mile and three quarters is Wood creek, the bed of which is used to its entrance into lake Oneida, the distance along its meanders being 23 miles, but in the line in which a canal might be cut, only 14 miles, and the fall 60 feet,   14   60

The Oneida forms a natural canal of twenty miles in length, and communicates by the Onondago   20

| *Carried forward,* | 34 | 60 |

	DIST.	FALL:
	Miles.	*Feet.*
Brought forward,	34	60

and Oswego rivers with lake Ontario. The distance by water down those two rivers to Oswego, on lake Ontario, is 63 miles. The upper part of the navigation is generally good, but the last 12 miles from the Oswego falls, which are not passable, to lake Ontario, are a continued rapid. The fall from lake Oneida to lake Ontario has not been ascertained by actual measurement, but is estimated at 130 feet. From Rotterdam, on lake Oneida, to the mouth of Salmon creek on lake Ontario, a few miles east of Oswego, the distance is 22 miles; and the ground being favorable, it is expected that the line of canal would not exceed 26 miles,

	26	130
	60	190

The elevation of the summit level between the Mohawk and the waters of lake Ontario, being only 390 feet above the tide water at Troy, and 190 feet above lake Ontario, a canal navigation is practicable the whole distance. Whether this should be attempted for a sloop or boat navigation, must depend principally, if not altogether, on the supply of water. It is stated that the canal from the summit level to Troy, must necessarily follow the valley of the Mohawk, and perhaps occasionally enter and cross the river. Calculated for a boat navigation, the expense may be estimated as followeth:

Dollars,

Mr. Weston estimated the expense of a canal, from Lansing mills to tide water at Troy, around the Cohoes falls, at   250,000

The distance from the summit level to Lansing mill is 120 miles, and to lake Ontario, deducting the 20 miles occupied by lake Oneida, 40 miles, together 160 miles of canal, the digging of which at 8000 dollars a mile, is   -   - $ 1,280,000

The fall from the summit level to Lansing mills is 250 feet, and to lake Ontario 190 feet, together 440 feet lockage, which will require 55 locks of eight feet lift each. These at 7,500 dollars, the cost of the stone locks erected by the company at the Little falls, will cost about   -   -   -   -   -   420,000

Feeder and aqueducts may be estimated at   ..   -   -   -   -   250,000

Making altogether two millions two hundred thousand dollars.   -   -   2,200,000

It is not believed that a sloop navigation, if practicable, could be effected for a less sum than five millions of dollars. The following works have already been completed by the company :

At the Little falls a canal three quarters of a mile in length, has been opened, and a descent of 42 feet effected by six locks of solid masonry, each of which is 70 feet long, and 12 feet wide. At the German flats, four miles above the Little falls, another canal one mile in length, with two stone locks of the same materials and dimensions, effects a descent of ten feet.

On the summit level a canal one mile and three quarters in length, and supplied with water from the river Mohawk by a short feeder, unites that river and Wood creek, by means of two locks of the same dimensions and materials, one at each extremity of the canal. All those canals are 2 feet and a half deep, 24 wide at bottom, and 32 at top, and admit boats of ten tons. It is proper to state, that at first, wooden locks had been erected at the Little falls, and brick locks on the summit canal. At both places they had become totally unfit for service at the end of seven years, and it was necessary to replace them by stone locks: a circumstance which encreased considerably the expense of the undertaking.

Several minor improvements have been made on the Mohawk; and the navigation of Wood creek, of which the principal defect is want of water, has been improved by raising dams, and by the erection of four temporary wooden locks. But until a canal shall have been opened the whole distance from the summit level to lake Oneida, the navigation will be imperfect, and the profits inconsiderable.

The funds of the company do not enable them to undertake the necessary improvements at the two extremities of the line, a canal around the Cohoes falls to tide water, and another canal from lake Oneida to lake Ontario. The usual portage at the first place is from Schenectady to Albany; and a very good and expensive artificial road of 16 miles, made by another company, unites the two towns. Another company has lately been incorporated, for the purpose of making an artificial road at the other extremity of the line from Rotterdam, on lake Oneida, to Salmon creek on lake Ontario.

The capital of the company is 232,000 dollars, of which the state of New York owns 92,000; but with the exception of one dividend of 3 per cent. all the tolls have been applied to the works; and including these and a debt of 20,000 dollars due by the company, the whole expenditure amounts to 370,000 dollars. The annual tolls do not yet exceed 13,000 dollars.

III. NIAGARA.

THE fall from lake Erie to lake Ontario has already been stated at 450 feet. A company had also been incorporated by the state of New York, for the purpose of opening a canal at this place: but it does not appear that any thing ever was attempted after the survey had been made. The intention seems to have been to open a canal navigation for boats only, from fort Schlosser to Devil's hole; the lake itself and Giles's creek would have supplied the water, and the expense was estimated at 437,000 dollars.

It is however evident that the canal, in order to be as eminently useful as the nature of the undertaking seems to require, should be on such scale as to admit vessels which can navigate both lakes. Considering the distance, which in that case must be extended to about ten miles, and the lockage of 450 feet, it is not believed that the expense can be estimated at less than 1,000,000 dollars.

THE works necessary to effect water communications between the tide water of the North river, the St. Laurence, and all the lakes, (lake Superior only excepted) are therefore estimated at four millions of dollars, viz.   *Dollars.*

Northern navigation to lake Champlain, - - - - - - -	800,000
Western navigation to lake Ontario,	2,200,000
Falls of Niagara for a sloop navigation,	1,000,000
	4,000,000

The papers relative to those communications will be found under the letter (B.); but the utility of these will not be confined to the extensive navigation of the lakes themselves. For the mountains being completely turned, when arrived into lake Erie, the ridge which separates the waters emptying into that and into lake Michigan, from the northern branches of the Ohio, and from the waters of the Mississippi, is of a moderate elevation, and is gradually depressed in its course westwardly. There is no doubt of the practicability of opening canals at a future period, between several of those waters, either by selecting proper levels, or by means of short tunnels across favorable parts of the ridge. It will at present be sufficient to point out the principal communications now in use.

The distance from lake Erie to lake Chetoughe, an extensive and important elevated reservoir, which is the source of the Canowango branch of the Allegheny, is seven miles by a continual ascent, the elevation of which is not ascertained.

From Presqu' isle on lake Erie, to Le Beuf on French creek, another branch of the Allegheny, the distance is sixteen miles, and a company is incorporated by the state of Pennsylvania, for making an artificial road across that portage.

The navigation from lake Chetoughe, and from Le Beuf to Pittsburgh, offers no impediment whenever the waters are high; and the greater part of the salt now consumed in the north-west counties of Pennsylvania, as far as Pittsburgh, and some distance down the Ohio, is brought from the salt springs of New York, by Oswego, through lake Ontario; then across the portage of Niagara to lake Erie, and thence by either of the two last mentioned portages to the waters of the river Allegheny.

The distance from the place where the Cayuga, a river emptying into lake Erie, ceases to be navigable, to the navigable waters of the Muskingum, which empties into the Ohio 170 miles below Pittsburgh, is only six miles; and a company is said to be formed for the improvement of that communication.

Sandusky river and the Scioto take their sources in the same swamp. The navigation of the Miami of lake Erie is interrupted by some falls; but its upper branches approach those of the Miami of the Ohio, and of the Wabash, and are stated as being nearly on the same level.

The Illinois river, which empties into the Mississippi above St. Louis, rises in a swamp, which when the waters are high, affords a natural canoe navigation to the sources of Chicago creek, a short stream, which falls into lake Michigan, at its southern extremity.

Another communication generally used by the Indian traders is that from Green bay, also in lake Michigan, to the Mississippi, by Fox river, and the Ouisconsing. Nor is there any doubt that if the inland navigation between the North river and the lakes was completely opened, the whole Indian trade either of the Mississippi by lake Michigan, or of the north-west by lake Superior, must necessarily center in an Atlantic port of the United States; a consideration of minor importance as a commercial object, when compared with the other advantages of that great communication, but of great weight in its relation to the political intercourse of the United States, with the Indians.

INTERIOR CANALS.

UNDER this denomination will be included all the canals of which any knowledge has been obtained, and which are not immediately on the rivers opening communications with the western waters or with those of the St. Laurence, although some of them may be considered as extending those communications to more remote sea ports. The documents from which the information is extracted will be found under the letters (C. c.)

I. Merrimack.

THE navigation of that river, which rising in the state of New-Hampshire, falls into the sea at New-buryport after a course of 180 miles, is interrupted by several falls. A canal called Blodget's canal has been opened around Asmoskeag falls. Lower down and about 40 miles from the sea, the Essex canal, 4 miles in length, and admitting boats drawing 3 feet and a half, will open a communication around the Patucket falls, effecting through 3 locks, a descent of 34 feet. From the lower extremity of the canal, the river is navigable to the head of the tide at Haverhill, although the fall be 45 feet within that distance. No particular account has been received of the capital expended; but it is believed that the work will be profitable to the undertakers.

The Middlesex canal, uniting the waters of that river with the harbor of Boston, is however the greatest work of the kind which has been completed in the United States.

That canal, 12 feet wide and 3 1-2 feet deep, draws its supply of water from Sudbury or Concord river, a branch of the Merrimack, and from the summit ground extends six miles with a descent of 28 feet to the Merrimack above the Patucket falls, and 22 miles with a descent of 107 feet to the tide water of the harbour of Boston. The descent to the Merrimack is effected by three, and that to tide water, by nineteen locks. They are all 90 feet long, 12 feet wide, of solid masonry and excellent workmanship.

In order to open that canal, it was necessary to dig in some places at the depth of 20 feet, to cut through ledges of rocks, to fill some vallies and morasses, and to throw several aqueducts across the intervening rivers. One of these across the river Shawshine is 280 feet long, and 22 feet above the river. All those obstacles have been overcome, and boats of 24 tons, 75 feet long and 11 feet wide, can navigate the canal. Those in most general use are of smaller dimensions, and are drawn by two horses at the rate of three miles an hour. A raft of one mile in length and containing eight hundred tons of timber, has been drawn by two oxen, part of the way at the rate of one mile an hour. Common boats pass from one end of the canal to the other in 12 hours. The capital expended on the work is stated at 478,000 dollars, and the water rights and necessary land cost a further sum of 58,000 dollars. The total expense has exceeded 550,000 dollars : the tolls have never yet exceeded 17,000 dollars a year, but are encreasing.

Several other canals have been contemplated in the state of Massachusetts, intended to unite the waters of Providence or Patucket river, with those of Charles river, which falls into the harbor of Boston, and of the river Connecticut. The grounds have been surveyed, but no particular description h.s been obtained, and the works have not yet been commenced.

II. Schuylkill and Delaware.

A Company was incorporated several years ago by the state of Pennsylvania, for opening a canal from Norristown, on the river Schuylkill, to the tide water of the Delaware at Philadelphia. The distance is 16 miles, the fall 53 feet, and the canal deriving its water from the Schuylkill, would have been carried on a level to Philadelphia, and in its descent to the Delaware supplied the city with water, and the shipping with docks. The expense had been estimated at 533,000 dollars; the work was commenced, one third part of the digging effected, and a considerable sum expended. But either from want of funds, or from an improper selection of the ground, or from other causes not fully understood, the undertaking if not altogether abandoned, has been suspended for several years.

This canal was intended as the first link of an extensive western communication. The Schuylkill, from Norristown to Reading, 46 miles higher up the river, being navigable a great portion of the year, was considered as the next link.

III. Schuylkill and Susquehannah.

Another company was incorporated, for the purpose of opening an inland navigation between Reading, on the Schuylkill, to Middletown, on the Susquehannah. Both towns are in the great Lime stone valley, beyond the Blue Ridge, and the distance is 70 miles. It had been at first supposed that it would be sufficient to cut a canal four miles in length, on the summit level between the two rivers; and thereby to unite the Tulpehocken which falls into the Schuylkill, with the Quitipahilla, a branch of the Swatara, which empties into the Susquehannah. But it was soon ascertained that the original plan of improving by a succession of dams the navigation of those small rivers was erroneous, and that it would be necessary to cut a canal the whole way.

The summit level is at an elevation of 310 feet above the Schuylkill, and of 308 feet above the Susquehannah. Adjacent springs are considered sufficient for the upper locks: and the creeks would after a short descent afford an abundant supply. The proposed dimensions of the canal were a breadth of 20 feet at the bottom, and a depth of 3 feet and a half: and the expense was estimated at near 1,500,000 dollars.

The work was commenced: the canal has been cut the whole distance of 4 miles on the summit level; five locks made of brick have been constructed; land and water rights have been purchased, and a considerable capital has been expended. But although the state of Pensylvania has permitted the company to raise 266,000 dollars by lottery, and is bound to pay to them 300,000 dollars whenever the work shall have been completed, it remains suspended for want of funds.

The great lockage necessary for this canal, is the principal objection to that line of communication: and it has·been suggested that a canal from Columbia, on the Susquehannah, to tide water or to the great Delaware and Chesapeake canal, would be much less expensive, and equally beneficial both to the interior country and to Philadelphia. This question, as many others suggested in this report, cannot be decided by any but practical and skilful engineers.

IV. Appomattox.

A Company has been incorporated for opening a canal from the upper end of the falls of that river, which is the south branch of James River, to Petersburgh on the head of the tide. The distance is five miles, and the descent more than thirty feet to a bason, about 60 feet above the tide, in which the canal will terminate. The water is drawn from the river; and the canal 16 feet wide, 3 feet deep, and admitting boats of 6 tons, is nearly completed. The capital already expended amounts to sixty thousand dollars. But the company own thirty negroes, and suppose that their labor, and a further sum of ten thousand dollars, will be sufficient to build the locks, and to dig about half a mile which remains to be cut in order to open the communication between the river and the bason. This work which has been carried on with much zeal, and at a small expense, will open an important navigation of near 100 miles.

V. Neuse and Beaufort.

The harbor of Beaufort, in North Carolina, and which must not be confounded with that of the same name in South Carolina, admits vessels drawing eighteen feet of water. Ocracoke inlet the only navigable entrance into the Pamtico and Albemarle sounds, that extensive estuary of the rivers Chowan, Roanoke, Tar and Neuse, has less water, and is 70 miles from Newbern, on the last mentioned river. The distance between Newport, or Beaufort river and the Neuse, being only three miles, and the elevation of the highest intervening ground no more than seven feet above tide water, a canal uniting the two rivers, was undertaken by a company incorporated for that purpose by the state of North Carolina. All the shares have, from particular circumstances, become the property of one individual; and the work which had been commenced some years ago, is now suspended.

VI.   Cape Fear River.

A Company incorporated by the same state, for improving the navigation of this river, after having exhausted a portion of their funds, which did not exceed twelve thousand dollars, in fruitless attempts to improve the natural navigation of the river, have opened a canal with a lock, which opens a safe passage around the Buck horn or great falls, seven miles below the junction of the Deep and Haw river. Another canal, six miles in length, with two locks, is necessary around Smilie's falls. Nearly half that distance has been completed; but the work is now suspended for want of funds. The legislature has lately authorised the company to encrease their capital.

VII.   New Orleans.

The canal Carondelet, which has already been mentioned, extends from Bayou St. John, to the fortifications or ditch of the city, and thereby opens an inland communication with lake Pontchartrain. A company is incorporated by the territorial legislature, for the purpose of repairing and improving that work and of uniting the canal by locks with the Mississippi. Independent of other advantages, this undertaking would enable government to transport with facility and use the same naval force for, the defence of both the Mississippi and lake Pontchartrain, the two great avenues by which New Orleans may be approached from the sea.

TURNPIKE, OR ARTIFICIAL ROADS.

A great number of artificial roads have been completed in the eastern and middle states, at an expense varying from less than one thousand to fourteen thousand dollars a mile. The labor bestowed on the least expensive species consists in shortening the distance, diminishing the ascent of hills, removing rocks, levelling, raising and giving a proper shape to the bed of the roads, draining them by ditches, and erecting bridges over the intervening streams. But the natural soil of the road is used, instead of covering it with a stratum of gravel or pounded stones.

It appears by one of the papers marked (**D.**) under which letter will be found all the information which has been obtained respecting roads, that fifty turnpike companies have been incorporated, since the year 1803, in the state of Connecticut alone; and that the roads undertaken by those companies are all of that description. Thirty nine of those roads extending together 770 miles, are completed. The most expensive is that from New Haven to Hartford, which has cost 79,261 dollars; or the distance being 34 miles and three quarters, at the rate of 2,280 dollars a mile: but about 18,000 dollars of the capital have been expended in the purchase of the land through which the road is carried. The nett income on this road, deducting the annual repairs and expenses from the annual tolls, does not exceed 3000 dollars. Of six of the roads, which together extend 120 miles, no account has been received. The other thirty two extend together 615 miles, and have cost only 340,000 dollars, or on an average at the rate of 550 dollars a mile : and it seems that the aggregate of annual tolls on the whole is 86,000 dollars ; from which deducting the annual repairs and expenses, amounting to 48,000 dollars, leaves a nett income of 38,000 dollars, or of about eleven per cent. on the capital expended.

No particular account has been received of the roads in the other eastern states; but it is known that besides some of a similar description with those of the state of Connecticut, several of a more expensive kind have been completed, particularly in Massachusetts. The cost has varied from 3000 to 14,000 dollars a mile ; and amongst artificial roads of the first grade may be mentioned those from Boston to Providence, to Salem, and to Newburyport. These are all covered with an artificial stratum of gravel or pounded stones, and finished in the most substantial manner. Great expense has also been incurred in order to shorten the distance without exceeding the angle of ascent, which is fixed at 5 degrees ; and it is stated that the road to Newburyport, 32 miles in length, and in which marshes and rocks presented considerable obstacles, has cost 400,000 dollars, or at the rate of 12,500 dollars a mile. Those expensive roads, however useful and permanent, appear to be much less profitable than those of Connecticut. The Salem road is said to yield six per cent. another road has been stated as yielding eight per cent. the income of all the others in the state of Massachussetts, is said not to exceed on an average three per cent. and that of the road from Boston to Newburyport, amounts to no more than two per cent.

A greater capital has been vested on turnpike roads in the state of New York, than in any other. In less than seven years, sixty seven companies have been incorporated, with a nominal capital of near five

millions of dollars, for the purpose of making more
than 3000 miles of artificial roads; and twenty one
other companies have also been incorporated with a
capital of 400,000 dollars; for the purpose of erecting
21 toll bridges.   Although no particular account has
been received either of the capital actually expended,
of the annual amount of tolls, or of the materials of
the roads, it is known that great progress has been
made: and it has been stated that nine hundred miles
of road were already completed by 28 companies,
whose capital amounted to 1,800,000 dollars, and
who had 200 miles of road more to finish.

Those roads extend in every direction, but particularly from every town or village on the North
river, westwardly and north-westwardly, towards the
waters of the Susquehannah, and those of the great
lakes.   The most expensive is that from Albany to
Schenectady, fourteen miles long, and which has
cost at the rate of ten thousand dollars a mile.   Near
140 miles of roads extending westwardly from Albany
and Schenectady, appear to have cost at the rate of
2,500 or 3,000 dollars a mile.   The expense of all
the others does not seem on an average to exceed
1,250 dollars a mile.

More detailed information has been obtained respecting the roads in New Jersey, Pennsylvania and
Maryland.

In New Jersey a turnpike road has lately been
completed from Trenton to Brunswick.   The distance is 25 miles; the greatest angle of ascent 3
degrees, and the road is nearly in a straight line, the
only considerable obstruction being the " Sand
Hills," through which it was necessary to dig at the
depth of thirty feet, in order not to exceed the angle
of ascent.   The road is 36 feet wide, fifteen feet of
which are covered with about 6 inches of gravel.   A
few wooden bridges with stone abutments and piers
have been erected across the intervening streams.
The whole expense is stated at 2,500 dollars a mile.
From Brunswick the road will be extended to Eliza-

beth town, and the work is now progressing. Another road has been undertaken in the same state from Brunswick to Easton, on the river Delaware. The distance is 43 miles, of which eleven have been completed at an expense of 40,000 dollars. This road will be more expensive than the preceding, both on account of the ground, the bridges being more numerous, and the Blue Ridge, (Musconekong mountain) intervening : and because a more substantial facing or greater thickness of gravel is requisite. The funds of the company are exhausted.

In Pennsylvania artificial roads of the most substantial kind, have been completed, or are progressing, from Philadelphia, in sundry directions.

The principal are to Bristol and Trenton, 12 miles of which are completed ; to Germantown and Perkiomen, with two branches to Willow Grove, and to Chesnut Hill ; and to Lancaster and Columbia, with a branch to Harrisburgh.

The distance from Philadelphia to Perkiomen is 25 miles and a quarter ; the two branches extend, one 10 miles and the other 7 miles and a half; making together, near 43 miles. The angle of ascent is 4 degrees ; the breadth of the road fifty feet, of which 28 feet, having a convexity of 15 inches, are covered with a stratum either of gravel 18 inches thick or of pounded stones 12 inches thick. One half of the stones forming the lower part of the stratum, are broken into pieces not more than five inches in diameter : the other half or upper part of the stratum consists of stones broken into pieces not more than two inches and a half in diameter : and this difference in the size of the stones is represented as a considerable defect. Side or summer roads extend on each side of the gravel or stone road. The five miles next to Philadelphia have cost at the rate of 14,517 dollars a mile. The other 20 miles and a half at the rate of 10,490 dollars a mile. Yet there were no natural impediments, and only small bridges or culverts were necessary. The capital expended on these

25 miles and a half is 285,000 dolls.: the tolls amount to 19,000 dollars: the annual repairs and expenses to 10,000 dollars: the nett income to about 9,000 dollars, or little more than 3 per cent. on the capital expended.

The distance from the Schuylkill, at Philadelphia, to Lancaster, is 62 miles and a quarter. Exclusively of the side or summer roads, twenty four feet of the bed of the road are covered with a stratum of pounded stones 18 inches thick in the middle of the road, and decreasing each way to 12 inches. The Valley hills are the most elevated and steep on the road; but the angle of ascent no where exceeds 4 degrees. Stone bridges have been erected across all the intervening streams. That across the river Conestogo consisting of nine arches, is private property; and the most expensive built by the company, is that across the Brandywine, consisting of three arches of solid masonry, and which cost 12,000 dollars. The capital of the company amounted to 360,000 dollars; but this being insufficient, it became necessary to apply a considerable portion of the tolls to the completion of the work. The whole expense amounts to 465,000 dollars, or at the rate of about 7,500 dollars a mile. The annual tolls have not yet exceeded 25,000 dollars; and the annnual repairs and expenses are estimated at 13,000, leaving a nett income of about 12,000 dollars. The prospect of an increased profit, derived from the proposed extension of the road, has however raised the price of that stock nearly to par.

The Lancaster road, the first extensive turnpike that was completed in the United States, is the first link of the great western communication from Philadelphia. It has been extended ten miles westwardly to Columbia on the Susquehannah, and another branch is now progressing northwestwardly to Harrisburgh, also on the Susquehannah, and 36 miles from Lancaster. The state of Pennsylvania has also incorporated two companies in order to extend the road by two different routes as far as Pittsburgh on the Ohio, and near 300 miles from Philadelphia.

The southern route, following the main post road, passes by Bedford and Somerset. The northern route passes by Huntingdon and Frankstown, the highest point to which the Juniata branch of the Susquehannah is navigable. To this route the state has authorised a subscription of one hundred thousand dollars.

Other roads in a north-west direction from Philadelphia, towards the Genessee and Presqu'isle on lake Erie, are also progressing, and have been encouraged by the subscriptions or donations of the legislature. They are generally on a much less expensive plan than those in the direction of Pittsburgh. A section of 30 miles from Lausanne on the Lehigh, to Nescopeck on the Susquehannah, has been completed at the expense of 36,000 dollars, by a company; and it is intended to extend it 70 miles further to Newton, on the Tioga branch of the Susquehannah.

In Maryland, roads extending from Baltimore in various directions, have lately been undertaken by several companies and are rapidly progressing. On the falls turnpike, which extends in a northerly direction, about four miles of a road 22 feet wide, covered with a stratum of pounded stones 10 inches thick, and having an ascent not exceeding 4 degrees, have been completed at the rate of 7,500 dollars a mile.

The " Reister town" turnpike, in a northwestwardly direction, extends 16 miles to that village; whence two branches extending one 19 and the other 29 miles farther, will enter Pennsylvania at two different places. The road 24 feet wide, is covered with a stratum 12 inches thick, of pounded stones not more than 3 inches in diameter. The angle of ascent does not exceed 3 degrees and a half. Ten miles have been completed at the expense of 10,000 dollars a mile, and the work is progressing. The capital of the company amounts to 420,000 dollars.

The capital of the " Frederick town" turnpike company amounts to 500,000 dollars; and the company is authorised to open the great western road, as far as Boonsborough, beyond the Blue Ridge, and 62 miles from Baltimore. The angle of ascent will not exceed 4 degrees; the road has a convexity of 9 inches, and on a breadth of 22 feet is covered with a stratum 10 inches thick of pounded stones, not exceeding 3 inches in diameter, over which are spread two inches of gravel or coarse sand. The first 20 miles next to Baltimore have cost at the rate of 9,000 dollars, and the next 17 miles are contracted for at the rate of 7,000 dollars a mile.

The distance from Boonsborough to Cumberland, at the foot of the Allegheny mountain, following the present road is 73 miles , and although the company is not yet authorised to extend the turnpike to that place, the ground has been surveyed, and it is ascertained that the road may be continued with an angle of ascent not exceeding 4 degrees. The ascent of the road laid out by the United States from Cumberland to Brownsville, on the Monongahela, does not exceed 5 degrees, and the distance is 72 miles : making the whole distance of a turnpike road from Baltimore to the navigable waters of the Ohio, 207 miles. The distance from the City of Washington to the same spot on the Monongahela is some miles shorter, being as has already been stated, the shortest communication between tide water and the navigable western waters.

South of the Potomac few artificial roads have been undertaken. From Alexandria one is now progressing in a northwestwardly direction towards Middleburgh. Another has lately been commenced from Richmond to Ross's coal mine. But the only one which, so far as any accounts have been received, is completed, extends 12 miles from Manchester, opposite to Richmond, in a westwardly direction to the coal mines of Falling creek. This road, 36 feet wide is gravelled and has cost 50,000 dollars : but the last 4 miles did not cost more than at the rate of 3000 dollars a mile. Yet it is sufficiently substantial, the route being very level, to admit waggons carrying four tons.

The greater progress made in the improvement of roads in the northern parts of the union, must be principally ascribed to a more compact population, which renders those improvements more necessary, and at the same time supplies with greater facility the means of effecting them. The same difference is perceptible in the number of bridges erected in the several states.

In the eastern states, and particularly Massachusetts, wooden bridges uniting boldness to elegance, and having no defect but want of durability, have been erected over the broadest and deepest rivers. In the lower counties of Pennsylvania stone bridges are generally found across all the small streams. Both in that state, and at some distance eastwardly, bridges with stone piers and abutments, and a wooden superstructure are common over wide rivers. Of these the most expensive, and which may be considered as the first in the United States, is the permanent Schuylkill bridge near Philadelphia, erected by a company at an expense of 300,000 dollars. Its length including the abutments does not exceed 750 feet, and it is supported only by two piers and the abutments. But those piers, 195 feet apart, are of the most solid workmanship, and one of them was sunk at a depth of more than 24 feet below low water. The bridge is 42 feet wide, and the wooden superstructure is enclosed and covered with a shingle roof.

The want of bridges south of Pennsylvania, even on the main post road, is sensibly felt. One lately thrown across the Potomac 3 miles above the city of Washington, and which without any intervening piers is wholly suspended to iron chains extending from bank to bank, deserves notice on account of the boldness of its construction, and of its comparative cheapness. The principle of this new plan, derived from the tenacity of iron, seems applicable to all rapid streams of a moderate breadth.

The general principles of improved roads seem to be: 1st, the reduction of hills by diminishing the angle of ascent, which ought not to exceed, whenever practicable, 3 degrees and a half, and under no circumstances five degrees: 2d, a sufficient convexity in the bed of the road, together with ditches and drains, all which are intended to prevent the injury caused by standing water or freshets: 3d, an artificial bed of pounded stones or gravel sufficiently substantial to support the weight of the carriages in general use on the road, either for the conveyance of persons, or for the transportation of merchandize.

On the last point it appears from the facts already stated, or scattered in the communications received on that subject: 1st, That the stones ought to be similar in quality and reduced to the same size, which should not exceed three inches in diameter: 2d, That the preferable qualities of stone, rank in the following order—hard black stone, granite, flint, or quartz, blue lime stone, white ditto: 3d, That the stratum may be either of pounded stones 12 inches thick, or of pounded stones 10 inches thick, with 2 inches of gravel spread over the stones; or entirely of gravel 18 inches thick: 4th, That when the materials are equally convenient, the expense of those three modes will not materially differ, but that the rate of expense depends principally on the number of hills and bridges, distance of materials, breadth of the road, and price of labor: and 5th, That the general adoption of broad wheels for the transportation of heavy loads, is necessary to the full enjoyment of the advantages expected from the most substantial artificial roads. On the degree of convexity and on the proper shape to be given to the natural bed of the road under the artificial stratum, a diversity of opinions seems to prevail.

The roads heretofore made may be divided into three general classes.

1. Those where the only improvement consists in the reduction of hills, and in the convexity and

ditches of the road, whereby the angle of ascent is rendered more easy, and standing water excluded; but where the natural soil is used without any artificial stratum. The expense of these roads may vary according to local circumstances, and the perfection of the work, from five hundred to one thousand dollars a mile. They are most generally in use in the eastern states, and may be introduced with advantage in all those districts of country, where wealth does not admit more expensive improvements, or where the materials of an artificial stratum are altogether wanting. It is only in the last case, that they may be considered as a national object; and no other improvement besides bridges and causeways, is perhaps practicable in the lower country of the southern states. Iron, and even timber rail roads, may however be sometimes substituted in those level parts of the country, where stones and gravel are not to be found.

2. Roads prepared as above, of a reduced breadth, and covered with a thin coat of gravel not more than six or nine inches thick; such as the turnpike lately made between Trenton and Brunswick. These roads, the expense of which may be estimated at about 3000 dollars a mile, may be used wherever the frost does not materially affect them, and in every climate, when they are intended principally for the conveyance of persons, and not for the transportation of heavy loads.

3. The artificial roads of the best contruction, such as have been already described. These when not exceeding 22 feet in breadth, and except in the vicinity of large cities, will cost at the rate of 7000 dollars a mile, exclusively of bridges over large rivers. And they must be resorted to, whenever a *commercial* road for heavy transportation is intended, particularly in the middle states, or rather in the United States, between 41 and 36 degrees of north latitude. North of the 41st degree, the snow lies generally during the whole winter; and the great bulk

of heavy transportation is effected in sleighs during that season. There is therefore less necessity for using the roads in the spring; and they are also better protected against the effects of the frost by the snow. South of the 36th degree, which in the Atlantic states may be considered as the boundary of the great cotton cultivation, the frost does not materially injure the roads. It is between those two extremes that the most substantial are required; and it also happens that the great land communications with the western country, which considerably increase the amount of transportation, are principally within the same limits.

The same principles, which have directed the arrangement adopted in this report in relation to canals, will also point out those roads which seem in the first instance to claim the patronage of the general government.

Those which appear most necessary for the communications between the Atlantic and western rivers have already been mentioned under that head; and the improvement of the water communication between the North river and the great lakes ought to take the precedence of any other in that direction.

That road which therefore seems exclusively to claim public attention, is a great turnpike extending from Maine to Georgia in the general direction of the sea coast and main post road, and passing through all the principal sea ports. The general convenience and importance of such a work are too obvious to require any comments: and the expense seems to be the primary object of consideration.

The distance will be roughly estimated at 1,600 miles; and from what has been stated on the subject of roads generally, it may be inferred that the greater part of the road being intended almost exclusively for travelling, and not for transportation of heavy articles, the expense cannot exceed the rate of 3,000 dollars a mile. For although some detached portions of the route, being commercial roads, must be improved as such, and at a greater expense; an equivalent reduction in other parts will result from those portions which are already improved by private companies, and from the impossibility, for want of materials for an artificial stratum, of going in some places beyond what has been described as the first or cheapest species of turnpikes. The whole expense may therefore be estimated at 4,800,000 dollars.

A secondary object, but of more importance to government than to individuals, would be the improvement, on a much less expensive scale, of certain portions of roads leading to some points on the extremes of the union, intended principally for the purpose of accelerating the progress of the mail, and the prompt transmission of information of a public nature. The points contemplated, are Detroit, St. Louis in Upper Louisiana, and New Orleans. The portions of road which traversing a wilderness cannot be improved without the aid of the United States, are; from the Tuscarora branch of the Muskingum to Detroit; from Cincinnati, by Vincennes, to St. Louis; and from Nashville in Tennessee, or Athens in Georgia; to Natches. The expense necessary to enable the mail and even stages to proceed at the rate of 80 miles a day, may, at the rate of about 200 dollars a mile, including bridges over all the small streams, be estimated for those three roads, at 200,000 dollars.

RECAPITULATION AND RESOURCES.

THE improvements which have been respectfully suggested as most important, in order to facilitate the communication between the great geographical divisions of the United States, will now be recapitulated; and their expense compared with the resources applicable to that object,

I. From north to south, in a direction parallel to the sea coast :

Dollars.

1. Canals opening an inland navigation for sea vessels from Massachusetts to North Carolina, being more than two thirds of the Atlantic sea coast of the United States, and across all the principal capes, cape Fear excepted,   3,000,000
2. A great turnpike road from Maine to Georgia, along the whole extent of the Atlantic sea coast,   - - 4,800,000
                ——— 7,800,000

II. From east to west, forming communications across the mountains between the Atlantic and western rivers :

1. Improvement of the navigation of four great Atlantic rivers, including canals parallel to them,   - - 1,500,000
2. Four first rate turnpike roads from those rivers across the mountains, to the four corresponding western rivers,   2,800,000
3. Canal around the falls of the Ohio,   . - - 300,000
4. Improvement of roads to Detroit, St. Louis and New Orleans,   - - - 200,000
                ——— 4,800,000

III. In a northern and north westardly direction, forming inland navigations between the Atlantic sea coast, and the great lakes and the St. Laurence :

Brought forward, - 12,600,000

L Inland navigation between the North river and lake Champlain, - - 800,000

2. Great inland navigation opened the whole way by canals, from the North river to lake Ontario, - - - 2,200,000

3. Canal around the falls and rapids of Niagara, opening a sloop navigation from lake Ontario to the upper lakes, as far as the extremities of lake Michigan, - - - 1,000,000
                                                    ———————— 4,000,000

Making together, - - $ 16,600,000

IV. The great geographical features of the country have been solely adhered to in pointing out those lines of communication : and these appear to embrace all the great interests of the union, and to be calculated to diffuse and encrease the national wealth in a very general way, by opening an intercourse between the remotest extremes of the United States. Yet it must necessarily result from an adherence to that principle, that those parts of the Atlantic states through which the great western and north west communications will be carried, must, in addition to the general advantages in which they will participate, receive from those communications greater local and immediate benefits, than the eastern, and perhaps southern states. As the expense must be defrayed from the general funds of the union, justice, and perhaps policy not less than justice, seem to require that a number of local improvements, sufficient to equalize the advantages, should also be undertaken in those states, parts of states, or districts, which are less immediately interested in those inland communications. Arithmetical precision cannot indeed be ob-

tained in objects of that kind ; nor would an appor-
tionment of the monies applied, according to the
population of each state, be either just or practicable; since roads, and particularly canals, are often of
greater utility to the states which they unite, than
to those through which they pass. But a sufficient
number of local improvements, consisting either of
roads or canals, may without any material difficulty
be selected so as to do substantial justice, and give
general satisfaction. Without pretending to suggest
what would be the additional sum necessary for that
object, it will, for the sake of round numbers, be estimated at   -   -   -   -   -   3,400,000

Which added to the sum estimated
for general improvements,   -   16,600,000

Would make an aggregate of twen-
ty millions of dollars,   -   -   20,000,000

An annual appropriation of two million of dollars,
would accomplish all those great objects in ten years,
and may without inconvenience, be supplied in time
of peace, by the existing revenues and resources of
the United States. This may be examplified in several ways.

The annual appropriation on account of the principal and interest of the public debt, has, during the
last six years, amounted to eight millions of dollars.
After the present year, or at farthest, after the ensu-
ing year, the sum which, on account of the irre-
deemable nature of the remaining debt, may be applied to that object, cannot in any one year exceed
4,600,000 dollars, leaving therefore from that source
alone, an annual surplus of 3,400,000 dollars, applicable to any other object.

From the 1st January, 1801, to the 1st January,
1809, a period of eight years, the United States shall
have discharged about 34 millions of the principal of
the old debt, or deducting the Louisiana debt, incurred during the same period, and not yet discharg-

ed, about 23 millions of dollars. They may with equal facility, apply in a period of ten years, a sum of 20 millions of dollars, to internal improvements.

The annual permanent revenue of the United States, calculated on a state of general peace, and on the most moderate estimate, was in a report made to Congress on the 6th day of December, 1806, computed for the years 1809–1815, at 14 millions of dollars, The annual expenses on the peace establishment, and including the 4,600,000 dollars, on account of the debt, and 400,000 dollars for contingencies, do not exceed eight millions and a half, leaving an annual surplus of five millions and a half of dollars. To provide for the protection and defence of the country, is undoubtedly the object to which the resources of the United States, must, in the first instance be applied, and to the exclusion of all others, if the times shall require it. But it is believed, that in times of peace, (and to such period only are these remarks applicable) the surplus will be amply sufficient to defray the expenses of all the preparatory measures of a permanent nature which prudence may suggest, and to pay the sum destined for internal improvements. Three millions annually applied during the same period of ten years, would arm every man in the United States, fill the public arsenals and magazines, erect every battery and fortification which could be manned, and even, if thought eligible, build a navy. That the whole surplus would be inadequate to the support of any considerable increase of the land or naval force kept in actual service in time of peace, will be readily admitted. But such a system is not contemplated: if ever adopted, the objects of this report must probably be abandoned. For, it has not heretofore been found an easy task for any government to indulge in that species of expenses, which leaving no trace behind it, adds nothing to the real strength of the country, and at the same time to provide for either its permanent defence or improvement.

It must not be omitted that the facility of communications, constitutes, particularly in the United States, an important branch of national defence. Their extensive territory opposes a powerful obstacle to the progress of an enemy. But on the other hand, the number of regular forces, which may be raised, necessarily limited by the population, will for many years be inconsiderable when compared with that extent of territory. That defect cannot otherwise be supplied than by those great national improvements, which will afford the means of a rapid concentration of that regular force, and of a formidable body of militia, on any given point.

Amongst the resources of the union, there is one which from its nature seems more particularly applicable to internal improvements. Exclusively of Louisiana, the general government possesses, in trust for the people of the United States, about one hundred millions of acres fit for cultivation, north of the river Ohio, and near fifty millions south of the state of Tennessee. For the disposition of those lands a plan has been adopted, calculated to enable every industrious citizen to become a freeholder, to secure indisputable titles to the purchasers, to obtain a national revenue, and above all to suppress monopoly. Its success has surpassed that of every former attempt, and exceeded the expectations of its authors. But a higher price than had usually been paid for waste lands by the first inhabitants of the frontier became an unavoidable ingredient of a system intended for general benefit, and was necessary in order to prevent the public lands being engrossed by individuals possessing greater wealth, activity or local advantages. It is believed that nothing could be more gratifying to the purchasers, and to the inhabitants of the western states generally, or better calculated to remove popular objections, and to defeat insidious efforts, than the application of the proceeds of the sales to improvements conferring general advantages on the nation, and an immediate benefit on the purchasers and inhabitants themselves. It may be added, that the United States, considered merely as owners of the soil, are also deeply interested in the opening of those communications, which must necessarily enhance the value of their property. Thus the opening of an inland navigation from tide water to the great lakes, would immediately give to the great body of lands bordering on those lakes, as great value as if they were situated at the distance of one hundred miles by land from the sea coast. And if the proceeds of the first ten millions of acres which may be sold, were applied to such improvements, the United States would be amply repaid in the sale of the other ninety millions.

The annual appropriation of two millions of dollars drawn from the general revenues of the union, which has been suggested, could operate to its full extent only in times of peace and under prosperous circumstances. The application of the proceeds of the sales of the public lands, might perhaps be made permanent until it had amounted to a certain sum, and until the most important improvements had been effected. The fund created by those improvements, the expense of which has been estimated at twenty millions of dollars, would afterwards become itself a perpetual resource for further improvements. Although some of those first communications should not become immediately productive, and although the same liberal policy, which dictated the measure, would consider them less as objects of revenue to government, than of increased wealth and general convenience to the nation, yet they would all sooner or later acquire, as productive property, their par value. Whenever that had taken place in relation to any of them, the stock might be sold to individuals or companies, and the proceeds applied to a new improvement. And by persevering in that plan, a succession of improvements would be effected until every portion of the United States should enjoy all the advantages of inland navigation and improved roads, of which it was susceptible. To effect that great object, a disbursement of twenty millions of dollars, applied with more or less rapidity according to the circumstances of the United States, would be amply sufficient.

The manner in which the public monies may be applied to such objects, remains to be considered.

It is evident that the United States cannot under the constitution open any road or canal, without the consent of the state through which such road or canal must pass. In order therefore to remove every impediment to a national plan of internal improvements, an amendment to the constitution was suggested by the executive when the subject was recommended to the consideration of Congress. Until this be obtained, the assent of the states being necessary for each improvement, the modifications under which that assent may be given, will necessarily control the manner of applying the money. It may be however observed that in relation to the specific improvements which have been suggested, there is hardly any which is not either already authorised by the states respectively, or so immediately beneficial to them, as to render it highly probable that no material difficulty will be experienced in that respect.

The monies may be applied in two different manners: the United States may with the assent of the states, undertake some of the works at their sole expense; or they may subscribe a certain number of shares of the stock of companies incorporated for the purpose. Loans might also in some instances be made to such companies. The first mode would perhaps, by effectually controlling local interests, give the most proper general direction to the work. Its details would probably be executed on a more economical plan by private companies. Both modes may perhaps be blended together so as to obtain the advantages pertaining to each. But the modifications of which the plan is susceptible must vary according to the nature of the work, and of the charters, and seem to belong to that class of details, which are not the immediate subject of consideration.

At present the only work undertaken by the United States at their sole expense, and to which the assent of the states has been obtained, is the road from Cumberland to Brownsville. An appropriation may for that purpose be made at any time. In relation to all other works, the U. States have nothing at this time in their power but to assist those already authorised; either by loans or by becoming stockholders; and the last mode appears the most eligible. The only companies incorporated for effecting some of the improvements considered in this report as of national and first rate importance, which have applied for such assistance, are the Chesapeake and Delaware canal, the Susquehannah canal, and the Dismal swamp companies; and authority might be given to subscribe a certain number of shares to each, on condition that the plan of the work to be executed should be approved by the general government. A subscription to the Ohio canal, to the Pittsburgh road, and perhaps to some other objects not fully ascertained, is also practicable at this time.

As an important basis of the general system, an immediate authority might also be given to take the surveys and levels of the routes of the most important roads and canals which are contemplated: a work always useful, and by which the practicability and expense of the undertakings would be ascertained with much more correctness than in this report. A moderate appropriation would be sufficient for those several objects.

In the selection of the objects submitted in obedience to the order of the Senate, as claiming in the first instance the aid of the general government, general principles have been adhered to, as best calculated to surpress every biass of partiality to particular objects. Yet some such biass, of which no indivi dual is perfectly free, may without being felt, have operated on this report. The national legislature alone, embracing every local interest, and superior to every local consideration, is competent to the selection of such national objects. The materials contained in the papers herewith transmitted, and the information to be derived from surveys taken under the authority of the general government, will furnish the facts necessary for a correct decision. Two communications, by Mr. B. H. Latrobe, and by Mr. Robert Fulton, marked E. and F. are in the meanwhile respectfully referred to, as containing much interesting practical information, connected with observations of a general nature, on the subject.

All which is respectfully submitted.

ALBERT GALLATIN,
Secretary of the Treasury.

TREASURY DEPARTMENT,
4th April, 1808.

Circular Queries,

By the Secretary of the Treasury, in order to obtain information.

Note. All the documents were obtained in answer to those queries.

———————

QUERIES RESPECTING CANALS.

1. Points united by canal, and their distance by said canal.

2. Elevation of the highest ground through which canal passes; descent thence to the two extremities; and number of miles where canal is level.

3. Number, dimensions, contents, construction, and situation of locks.

4. Supply of water; whence obtained; its amount reduced to cubic feet per minute, hour or day; its elevation above the highest point of the canal; length of feeders; situation and contents of reservoirs. What additional resources may be resorted to if the present supply should fall short of the quantity wanted?

5. Designation of such parts of the route where the natural or improved bed of rivers is used.

6. Depth and breadth of canal; burthen of vessels; breadth of towing paths.

7. Aqueducts across valleys or rivers; tunnels through hills; bridges across the canal.

8. Particular obstructions and difficulties surmounted or to be encountered.

9. Defects either in the plan or execution, and the proposed remedies.

10. Estimate of the tonnage of vessels; species, weight and value of the articles annually conveyed by the canal; expense of carriage by canal, compared

with land or river carriage before canal was made: time employed in navigating through the whole canal.

11. Capital already expended, vested or wanted for completing the work.

12. Expenses per mile and in the whole, and as far as practicable, of every component part of the work in all its details.

13. Rate and gross amount of tolls ; annual expenses of repairs and contingencies ; annual nett income.

14. Substance of charters and acts of legislature on the subject.

QUERIES RESPECTING ARTIFICIAL ROADS.

1. Points united and their distance.

2. Elevation of the hills over which the road passes ; greatest angle of ascent which has been allowed.

3. Breadth, form, materials of the artificial road.

4. Bridges, their dimensions, materials, construction.

5. Particular obstructions and difficulties surmounted, or to be encountered.

6. Expenses per mile, and in the whole, and as far as practicable, of every component part of the work in all its details, viz. forming the bed of the road, cutting hills, quarrying, transporting, breaking, laying stones or gravel, &c.

7. Capital already expended, vested or wanted for completing the work.

8. Rate and gross amount of tolls ; annual expenses of repairs and contingencies ; annual nett income.

9. Substance of charters and acts of legislature on the subject.

Mr. Latrobe's Communication.

(E.)

Washington, March 16, 1808.

Sir,

I HAVE the honor of your letter of the 29th of July, 1807, transmitting to me a copy of the resolution of the Senate of the United States, of the 2d of March, 1807, together with a list of queries respecting artificial navigations, and canals, to which you request my answer and opinion.

In order to give you all the information on this subject which you wish, and I possess, and in the most condensed form, I ask your permission to depart from the order which your questions demand, and after treating the subject generally, to enter upon an account of those works, in detail, with which my personal experience has made me more particularly acquainted.

The most striking circumstance in a view of the Atlantic states of the union, in relation to the improvement of their internal navigation, is the uniformity of the natural arrangement of their rivers and mountains, and that this arrangement differs from that of ever other country in which artificial navigation has been attempted.

In other countries the general course of the rivers is between the mountains, and along the vallies; in this, the general course of the rivers is across that of the mountains and of the vallies. Our mountains, from their termination to the south-west in Georgia, hold a course to the east of north; the general direction of our principal rivers is to the east of south : and on inspection of the map, it will be observed, that as the direction of the mountains to the N. E. of the Delaware, becomes more easterly, so do our rivers acquire a more southern course, always crossing the mountains at nearly the same angle.

Our rivers may be divided into three classes;—*Primary rivers*, that discharge their water immediately into the ocean. Of these the relative magnitude might berated, according to the surface they respectively drain; *Secondary rivers*, or such as fall into the first, above their tide water; and *Creeks*, properly so called, which rise below the falls of the first rivers, or rather collect the water of the level land below the falls, and discharge it into the tide waters.

Of our primary rivers, the Susquehannah is the principal. By a great degree of geographical injustice, this mighty river loses its name at the foot of its falls, and is called, the Chesapeake bay, from thence to the ocean; although its width compared with its length, forbids the term of bay to be applied to what is called the Chesapeake. All of these rivers cross in the greatest part of their course the direction of the mountains. Of the *secondary rivers*, many of which are of great importance and magnitude, some and perhaps the greatest number hold a course parallel to the mountains, as the Shenandoah, the Conogocheague, the Lehigh, &c. draining the vallies, and receiving away the torrents of the mountains.

The third order of our water courses rise either in the lowest ridge of our hills, which I will call the granite ridge, and over which all our principal rivers, from Georgia to the Hudson, fall, and then run through the alluvial country which lies between the granite ridge and the ocean. Such rivers are, the Nottoway, the Blackwater, the Meherrin, the Annacosta, (eastern branch of Potomac) the Elk river, and the very important creek in the state of Delaware, the Christiana; or they are merely drains of the alluvial country, assuming an appearance of importance below the head of the tide, above which they are mere torrents, almost dry in the autumn. Such streams are all the rivers of the eastern shore of the

Chesapeake, and of the lower part of the Jerseys, and innumerable water courses, forming large estuaries in the southern states.

Our great north western lakes, from their first source to the eastern end of lake Erie, may be considered as part of the great river St. Laurence, following the direction of the rest of our rivers, until opposed by the northern extremity of the Allegheny. From thence its course follows the valley west of the Allegheny, through lake Ontario to the ocean, receiving the waters of the northern extremity of the mountain in its course.

This general view of the construction of our country was necessary in order to understand the general principles on which our artificial navigation can be so conducted, as to be useful, or even practicable ; and to explain why connections of waters, which on the map appear advantageous and feasible, would be useless, and perhaps impracticable, by any effort of art.

Two principal objects will dictate all the exertions towards the improvement of our internal navigation, which can for many years to come be attempted : 1. To carry our produce by water to the nearest port for its exportation, and the importation of foreign articles : 2. To exchange by internal commerce the articles reciprocally deficient on lines parallel to the sea coast. Canals, the use of which arises from manufacturing activity, will not probably be soon required.

The first object,—as all our principal rivers run seaward, and generally by the shortest course,—must be attained by the natural or improved navigation of the rivers themselves, or by canals cut parallel to them : the second may often require a navigation parallel to the vallies, so as to communicate one principal river with another.

The former attempt at improved navigation has already been made on many of our principal rivers,—the latter has been seldomer undertaken ; and only once above the falls of both primary rivers, in the canal intended to join the Susquehannah and Schuyl-kill, and the Schuylkill and Delaware rivers above Philadelphia.

The general construction of our country opposes to artificial navigation, in either of these directions, difficulties, which in no part of the world exist in so uniform, and certain a degree. Canals parallel to our rivers, have three formidable obstacles to encounter and overcome.

1. The rapid descent of the ravine cut through the mountains by the river itself, along which the canal must be carried ;—or, if the ravine be quitted, difficulties on the high levels, which, the further you go from the river, are always intersected by the more numerous ravines ; and embarrassed by the difficulty of returning to the ravine of the river.

2. The invariably rocky nature of the ground, which is uniformly of granite in all its varieties; and has numerous fissures which carry off the water, and require lining.

3. The difficulty of keeping off the land water, and of crossing the lateral branches and torrents of the river.

On the other hand, canals parallel to our mountains must necessarily cross the ridge or spur of the mountain which divides the waters of two primary rivers. On this ridge above the falls, the water requisite to supply the canal, is always scanty, often there is none : and though a tunnel or a stream engine, or in the last resort a rail road, are certain means of obviating the difficulty, they are expensive, inconvenient and imperfect. Below the granite ridge, the difficulty is less. There may always be found a supply of water from the ridge itself; and the feeders, though carried through rocky and expensive ground, are themselves useful as small canals, as far as they extend ; and below the ridge the soil is easily cut and embanked.

Having so frequently mentioned the granite ridge,

I will here trace its extent as far as my knowledge of our country enables me to do it.

The granite ridge forms the shore of the north side of Long island opposite to the island of New York. All the south of the island is alluvial, and is the first margin of alluvial soil below the granite ridge. This margin of alluvial soil beginning at Long island, widens as it extends to the south west, until in Georgia it becomes more than 200 miles in width.

Staten island and Bergen point, are two spurs of this same ridge, which continues nearly in the line of the post road to Trenton, where the river Delaware falls over it, having worn down the rocks more deeply there than many other of our rivers. The Delaware runs in its general direction for 60 miles under the ridge as far as New Castle, leaving it only for a short distance at particular bends of the river. At Philadelphia the ridge crosses the peninsula to Gray's ferry on Schuylkill. The softer granite of Schuylkill has been worn down so that the falls are 4 miles from its lower edge. From Philadelphia the ridge runs with the post road to Havre de Grace, where it is visible on both shores, although the tide extends 6 miles above, to the foot of the falls.

The Susquehannah, by the name of the Chesapeake, may be considered as running under the foot of the granite ridge almost as far as Baltimore, which city is built upon the foot of the ridge. At the river Patuxent, on the post road, the ridge appears again, but is lost under the incumbent soil, and is not again visible until it appears at Georgetown. The harder granite of the Potomac has resisted the force of the water more than the granite further to the north-east, and the tide reaches only 3 miles above its outrunnings. From the Potomac, the falls of Rappahannoc at Fredericksburgh, of James river at Richmond, Appomatox at Petersburg, Roanoke at Halifax, beyond which point my personal observation does not extend, point out the course of this ridge in a line nearly parallel to the Blue ridge, diverging to the eastward as it extends southward.

Of the improvement of the natural navigation of our rivers leading to the sea, and of canals cut parallel to them.

The difficulties of the natural navigation of our rivers are: In spring,—the danger of wreck in the wild water of our rapids; in autumn,—obstructions created by rocky shoals; and, in most of them, rapids and falls impracticable at all times. The least expensive and most obvious means of removing the former are the blowing of the most prominent rocks, so as to straighten the channel, and procure a passage at low water. This has in almost all our rivers been attempted on a greater or less scale, and with various degrees of success. When injudiciously performed, and in rivers of rapid descent, and liable to great variation in the quantity of their water, more injury has been done than advantage obtained. Many of our worst obstructions act as natural dams, which holding up the water, create a large extent of excellent navigation above them. Of this the James river above Westham, and the Susquehannah above Chickisalunga and Hunter's falls, are instances in point. Such obstructions when removed, let down the water rapidly from above, without supplying deeper navigation below.

In a river of such magnitude as the Susquehannah, indeed, no gap or sluice artificially cut, can materially affect the rapidity of the stream, but in lesser rivers, great care is required, not only to prevent lowering the water above, but to avoid giving a new direction to the current, more mischievous in its effects than that which has been changed. But with whatever judgment the natural navigation of a river perplexed by rapids and shoals may be conducted, and however its descent may be thereby facilitated, its ascent cannot possibly be rendered more easy, in the same degree. Thus for instance, although by the monies expended by the state of Pennsylvania and the Susquehannah canal company, on the natural navigation of the Susquehannah below Wright's ferry, it has been rendered much less dangerous to run down the distance of 41 miles, almost the whole of which is a tremendous rapid, from Columbia to the tide, and thereby to carry lumber, iron, and agricultural produce to Havre de Grace, and thence to Baltimore,—yet so difficult is the upstream navigation by the same route, even with the assistance of the Susquehannah canal, that the returns in imported articles have been generally purchased in Philadelphia and conveyed to Columbia or Middletown, above the rapids, by the Lancaster turnpike, thence to be boated to the country watered by the upper branches of the Susquehannah. And although the Philadelphia market has hitherto offered more advantages to the buyers of imported goods than that of Baltimore, yet the expense of transporting them 72 miles by land to Columbia, would, if there were a good navigation from Havre de Grace upwards, destroy this advantage.

The difficulty of carrying canals parallel to our great rivers, the scarcity of engineers possessing knowledge and integrity, the want of capital, and above all the erroneous dread of bold measures, and the fear of uselessly expending money in works hitherto unknown among us, has deterred those interested in improving our navigation, from deserting the beds of our rivers, while it was practicable to keep them. They have therefore had recourse to canals only where navigation was otherwise impossible; where obstructed by rocks, or broken by a cascade.

There cannot however be a reasonable doubt, that if in England, where, compared with the United States, the quantity of water in the rivers varies little between the driest and the wettest period of the year, a canal running parallel to a river, furnishes a much more certain and safe and equal and cheap navigation than the river itself—it is infinitely more the case here. Unfortunately those of our canals which have been cut to pass the rapids and falls of our rivers, partake in a great measure of the inconveniences of the rivers themselves; some wanting water when the river is low, some incapable of being entered excepting at a particular height of the water in the river, some subject to constant accumulation of bars, and all of those with which I am acquainted, much less useful than the money expended on them ought to have made them.

Those canals, of which I now particularly speak, are, the James river canal, the Potomac canal, the Conewago, and Susquehannah canals. Of the canals north of the Delaware, and south of Virginia, I have not sufficient knowledge, nor can I speak of the Appomattox canal. It is, I believe, not liable to the same strictures in all points, which I shall make upon the others, but though I am well acquainted with the ground, I have not seen the manner in which the work has been executed.

One great and fatal error has been interwoven into the scheme of the other canals, excepting only that of the Potomac: They have been dug as much with a view to the erection of mills, as to the purposes of navigation. To fit them for mill-races, their descent is rapid, and their current strong. They are liable, of course, to the variation of the quantity of water in the river; they bring down with their current, the alluvium of the river; bars are formed in them, as well by this alluvium, as by the land wash; and their banks, where they are not of rock, or walled, are liable to perpetual wear by the current. The canal is, besides, itself an inconvenient rapid to those who would ascend it.

Besides these inconveniencies, the contracts binding the company to furnish to the millers the water, when it rises above a certain gage-selle, for an annual rent, or on other fixed and permanent terms, tie the canal company to the original construction of the work, and forbid future improvement. For instance, if a lock were found to be useful above the highest mill, it could not be erected, because it would rob the mills below of their stipulated water; the inclination of the canal cannot be lessened, because it would have the same effect. In the James river canal, more than in any other which I have seen, this error, though now generally considered as a very great advantage, will at some future period be discovered and deplored. The Potomac canal, more especially that of the Little falls, has the same defect of a too rapid descent, although the object of a mill race is placed by their charter out of view. But its principal defect is of another kind, to which that of James river is also, but in a less degree, subject. It receives the wash of all the hills and ravines of the north bank, which ought to be discharged through culverts, or carried over bridges: and that legislative impartiality which has required the canal to enter the river at the very head of the tide, in order that Virginia may have an equal chance of becoming the depot of its commerce with Maryland, has very much injured its utility to the country at large.

In a still greater degree than the Potomac canal the Susquehannah canal, beginning at the Maryland and Pennsylvania line, and ending at the head of the tide, has the defect, not only of receiving the landwash of the hills and ravines, but also two considerable rivers, the Conewingo and Octorara, partaking this of all the danger arising from their inundations, and receiving their alluvium. This canal is also applied to the purposes of a mill race. Other inconveniences attend it, which arise from the most unfriendly nature of the river, and the local feelings of the state legislatures of Pennsylvania and Maryland, at the period of the incorporation of the company.

The Conewago canal, about 50 miles higher up the Susquehannah, is also a mill race, and is the roperty of an individual. It is of difficult entrace, which is to be regretted, as it ought to be the mans of passing a short but very dangerous fall of the river, which interrupts along extent of very good navigation.

Having thus pointed out the general and common defects of these canals, to which I may add the general want of proper slopes to their banks, I will now enter upon the very thankless task of giving an honest opinion respecting them in detail, viewing only the *public interests*, and perfectly conscious of the bearing of what I shall say, upon private feelings. These feelings, however, are extremely short-sighted; for nothing could be more advantageous to the individuals most interested, than those measures which would most benefit the public.

The James river and Appomattox canals stop short of tide water. The most important of these canals is that of James river. Upon the coal mines of James river our Atlantic sea ports will soon become dependent for their chief supply of fuel. That dependence exists already in respect to the fuel required for a variety of manufactures, and even now the smiths within 10 miles of our sea ports, require in order to carry on advantageous business, a supply of Virginian coal. There are three means (and I think only three)—by which the Virginian coal can be brought to the tide: 1. By a small canal and rail roads, immediately from the mines south of the river to the shipping tide water at Ampthill or its neighbourhood, along the valley of Falls creek : distance, I believe, 20 miles. This is a route easily practicable and at a moderate expense, for Falls creek rises in the coal mines themselves. 2. By the turnpike road to Manchester opposite Richmond. This road has been sometime completed, and is of the highest utility. 3. By James river to the head of the falls, and thence by the canal to Richmond. This is for two thirds of the coal country, the best and most obvious route. For from all the mines the coal may easily be brought to the river on rail roads, and thence boated, independently of the cheaper conveyance which Tuckahoe creek might be made to yield to a

great extent of coal land now little worked. But of
what adequate use is this navigation in boats carrying
at an average 200 bushels of coal only, when, if the
canal were well constructed, 1000 bushels might be
as easily and cheaply conveyed; and when, on their
arrival in Richmond, they must be unloaded, again
loaded into carts and carried down by a bad road to
the tide at Rockets, to be shipped? The Manchester
turnpike, with all its expense of waggons, horses, and
drivers, and the consequent waste of *labor*, *capital*,
food, and *forage*, is a better, and I am told, as cheap
a mode of conveyance.

The means by which the canal itself may be made
much more useful, I will not consume your time and
patience in detailing; what is most important, taking
the whole subject into view, is to connect the canal,
such as it is, with the tide.

In the year 1796, Mr. Weston, then engineer to
the western navigation companies of the state of New
York, was called to Richmond to give his advice and
opinion on this subject. It amounted to this: to
connect the basin with the foot of the falls, by a succession of ten or eleven locks in one tier, carrying
the race of Ross's mill upon an aqueduct across
the canal at the foot of the locks. With all defer-
ence to his talents, I cannot help remarking, that
of all expensive projects of which I ever heard, this
would have been one of the most useless. For independently of the excessive inconvenience and deten-
tion which such a tier of locks at the most busy part
of a navigation would occasion, the boats would arrive at their foot, in a very considerable rapid, now
impracticable, and which could only be made practicable by blowing up the rocky bed of the river.
When arrived there, two miles of tide water must be
encountered; to navigate which, these boats are
wholly unfit. I cannot help thinking that the present
mode of conveying the coal to Rockets is not much
less eligible. I refrain from stating many other objections, which are professional, and which I believe

were, as well as those already mentioned, as evident to Mr. Weston as to myself; but objections of another nature, more powerful than mere physical difficulties, opposed every project excepting that which he proposed.

In order to connect the basin of the James river canal with the tide, a very simple means is offered by the nature of the ground. To do this it will be necessary to form a capacious basin at Rockets, communicating with the tide by one or more locks. To carry a canal from thence along the level bank of James river to Shockoe creek. A cheap aqueduct of one arch of 30 feet span will carry the work across the creek into the back street. The canal will then go up the back street, mounting by successive locks, not more than two in each tier, into the basin. The canal from Rockets to the basin on Shockoe hill, should be of 9 feet draft of water, and the locks 100 feet long and 18 feet wide. This canal would of course bring vessels which navigate our coasts and bays and run out to the West India islands, into the basin on Shockoe hill.

The legislature of the state of Virginia, (for the commonwealth is deeply interested in the stock) has from time to time expressed great anxiety on the subject of completing this canal. But the dread of unforeseen difficulties and risks in carrying the work below the basin, and the value and productiveness of the stock in its present state, have hitherto over-balanced this anxiety. But considering Richmond as the principal source of fuel to the cities on our sea coast, at least until the mines of cape Breton shall supply us, I feel a national sentiment in deeply re-gretting the very fatal policy which maintains and supports the error, and the mutilation of this most important work. I will not at the same time deny, that when it is considered that those who projected and executed the canal were men of no acquaintance either with general science, or with this particular branch of art, and knew nothing of canals but from books or hearsay, they have already done wonders. They deserve the thanks of their state, and of the union. But the work should not stop where they have left it. Nature, has perhaps, done more for Richmond than for any scite where a city has been planted. For 10 miles above the city on both sides, and upon several islands of the stream, there are innumerable mill seats, supplied by one of the noblest rivers in the union. Immediately above the head of the falls lies an inexhaustible treasure of coal. Every art and manufacture to which human ingenuity can employ fire and water, may be here carried on with the least expense. From above, an easy and wide spreading navigation, collects on this spot all the raw materials which our climate can produce; below, a river capable of bearing sea vessels sufficient for every trade, but that across the ocean, is ready for the exportation of its merchandize. The town itself is placed on a healthy and commanding ground. But to improve these advantages to the utmost extent to which our population is equal, nothing would so much contribute as the completion of the Richmond canal.

I have dwelt specially on the coal trade to which this canal is subservient, as of first rate national importance. It is of no less importance to the state of Virginia as a means of conveyance of agricultural produce. As you will receive an answer in detail to your queries relative to the amount of all the sorts of produce carried upon it, and of its actual trade, I will not add any thing further to what I have already said on the subject, but to observe,—that at some distant period, the Chickahominy, a river rising in the coal country, and discharging itself into James river   miles below Richmond, where ships may take in their cargoes, offers a means of carrying down the coal destined for distant exportation.

A canal has often been projected for passing the falls of the Rappahannoc at Fredericksburg. There is no reasonable hope, however, that this work can soon be executed. The ravine of the river at the falls on either side is so abrupt, rocky, and irregular that great expense must be incurred to effect it,—an expense not likely to be repaid by its trade for many years.

A canal to connect the Rappahannoc with the Potomac, a few miles below Fredericksburg, across the northern neck, has also been spoken of. It would be a highly useful work, but would require a tunnel of 2 or 3 miles. I believe it could be executed at an expense not greater than the tolls would remunerate. Such a canal, however, does not belong to the class of which I am now speaking.

The Potomac canal consists of two parts,—one to pass the Great falls 14 miles above Georgetown,—the other to pass the Little falls. The errors committed in the construction of the work have been enumerated above. The trade of this canal, especially during the year 1807, has been so great, that there appears every prospect of its becoming a productive work,—*in those years* in which there is a considerable and equal quantity of water in the river. But upon this circumstance it must always depend. The information respecting it, which can be obtained from the company, on the spot, renders it unnecessary for me to say more upon it.

No attempt at the improvement of the navigation of any of the rivers of Maryland between the Susquehannah and the Potomac, has been made, nor is there in the prospects of advantage to be derived from the navigation of the two Patuxents, the Patapsco, or any of the lesser rivers falling into the Chesapeake, any thing which could at present tempt capital into such an undertaking.

But the Susquehannah itself has been for many years the object of almost all the attention directed in the states of Maryland and Pennsylvania to the improvement of our internal navigation. About 6 miles above Havre de Grace, this mighty river meets the tide. The place is now known by the name of

Smith's ferry. The map of the river from thence up to Wright's ferry (Columbia) in Pennsylvania, which I made in the year 1801, when directing the works carried on for the improvement of the natural bed of the river, and which by favor of the governor of Pennsylvania, I am able to exhibit with this memoir, will explain the nature of this part of the river very minutely, being drawn to a very large scale. The whole of this extent is one tremendous rapid, which in fact continues to the N. W. side of the Chickalunga hills, 3 miles above Columbia. The rapid is not every where of equal velocity, or equally dangerous. Wherever the river crosses a valley of limestone or slate, the rocks are worn down into a smoother and wider bed: but when it has to cross a ridge of granite, its course is immediately broken by irregular masses and range of rocks; its bed is narrow and enclosed by precipices, and its torrent furious and winding.

The Chickisalunga falls can be descended without danger, and no attempt to open them has been thought necessary. The ridge of granite hills through which they break, bounds on the N. W. the beautiful limestone valley of Columbia. Across this valley the river runs rapidly, but smoothly. Another narrow ridge of granite hills crosses the river immediately below Columbia, over which the river falls rapidly, and then enters the wider limestone valley known by the name of the Jochara valley. The river spreads here to the width of three miles, its stream is gentle though rapid, and it abounds in beautiful and fertile islands. It then suddenly contracts and is received into the narrow ravine which it has *sawed* down in the granite hill called Turkey hill. From its first entrance into the Turkey hill, to the tide, there is no part that deserves the name of a sheet of smooth water. When the river is full, the whole ravine about half a mile in width contains only one furious torrent in which few rocks comparatively are to be seen above the water; but the danger is not the less, and very skillful pilots, and many and stout hands are required to carry a boat or an ark safely down. But in the autumn, and in a dry season, the river itself can for 6 miles scarcely be seen, and its bed appears a barren and dry waste of irregular rocks, among which the loud roaring of water is only *heard:* for, from the Turkey hill to near the mouth of Conestogo, the whole river is discharged through a channel generally about 60 feet wide, in the greatest part of which the depth and the rapidity of the torrent is such, that it has not been fathomed. About a mile below the mouth of Conestogo, a narrow limestone valley touches the river on the N. E. side, but on the west shore not a trace of Limestone is to be seen. Four miles below Burkhalter's ferry, the river arrives at the high range of granite hills, abounding in copper, in which the gap mine is situated, and at a place called M'Call's ferry, it narrows to the width of 16 perches. Here I attempted to find bottom with a line of 180 feet, but failed, notwithstanding every precaution taken to procure a perpendicular descent of the weight attached to it. Through this pass the water is rapid, but smooth and safe. The river rises here rapidly and very suddenly after the fall of rain above; and it will never be possible to erect a safe bridge at this place, so often mentioned as the most practicable. The obstructions to navigation by 3 rapids below M'Call's, is not so considerable as to endanger the arks and boats that descend, until they arrive at the Baldfriar falls, below Peachbottom and about 8 miles above the tide. From M'Call's to the slate valley of Peachbottom, the river is filled with islands called the Bear islands. Across the valley of Peachbottom, and above the Baldfriar falls, the river is wide and safe. The best natural navigation, and that always pursued by boats descending by the natural bed of the river, is on the west side, from the foot of the bear islands. Above that point to Columbia, the best passage is on the east side. The most dangerous falls below Peachbottom were Amos's and Hector's falls, on which many wrecks annually occurred until the late improvements of the navigation were made.

From this description it may easily be imagined that if the descent of the river with boats loaded with produce was dangerous and difficult, the ascent was still more so. The natural obstructions were besides increased by fish-dams in every part of the river, and the rival interests of the states of Pennsylvania and Maryland prevented, for many years, every attempt at artificial improvement of the bed of the river. In the mean time each state took measures to go as far towards rendering the navigation of this river useful to their respective interests, as their means and limits would permit; and a company was incorporated in Maryland, to make a canal from the Maryland line to the tide, to pass all the obstructions of the river of the eight lowest miles; and in Pennsylvania two companies were also incorporated, the one to connect the Susquehannah with the Schuylkill, by a navigation taken out above all the dangerous falls, and the other to connect the Schuylkill with the Delaware. The objects of none of these companies were advantageously accomplished. The Susquehannah canal company have, however, completed a navigable canal, liable to the objections which I have above noticed. The Pennsylvania companies have made considerable progress in the works, under the direction of a very able engineer, Mr. Weston, but have not completed either canal so as to render them useful or productive.

At last, in the year 1801, the states of Maryland and Delaware having passed laws incorporating a company for the purpose of cutting a canal between the Chesapeake and Delaware, a former law of Pennsylvania, appropriating 10,000 dollars to the removal of obstructions in the Susquehannah, went into effect; and the late Colonel Fred. Antes, than whom no man was better fitted to accomplish its object, was charged with its execution. But he died on his arrival at the river, and the direction devolved upon me. The enclosed report to the legislature on this subject, details the extent of the work executed, and the principles on which I proceeded in the attempt to make a practicable and safe navigation both up and down the river. I will here only repeat that all my exertions were bent to force through all obstructions, a channel clear of rocks, of 40 feet wide, close to the Eastern shore, never leaving any rock upon which a vessel could be wrecked between the channel and the shore,—so that in the most violent freshes a boat should always be safe, by keeping close in shore. Rocks of immense magnitude were therefore blown away, in preference to the following a crooked channel more cheaply made, but more difficult and dangerous, and varying in safety and practicability, according to the degree of the rise of the river. There is however one part of the navigation in which the bed of the river must forever be pursued, namely, from the Indian steps above M'Call's to below the gap at M'Call's :—a part of the navigation, which, if art can conquer it, must be undertaken in a state of the country infinitely more abounding in wealth and population than at present.

Of the Chesapeake and Delaware Canal.

Having now answered that part of your inquiry which relates to the general subject of canals, I come to the particular merits of the Chesapeake and Delaware canal, of which you have requested me to give special information; together with my opinion on its location, unbiassed by any interests but those of the public.

The very able report of the committee to whom your letter to the president and directors of the company was referred, and who did me the honor to confer with me on the subject, conveys to you all the information which can be given of the history of the company, their pecuniary resources and difficulties, the motives that directed their choice in the location of the work, and the system under which it was begun and pursued. Every thing also that can be collected by the most indefatigable enquiry as to the probable proceeds of the canal, and the advantages it offers to those who have adventured in it, is also detailed; and there remains to me only the task of giving you that professional information, which as engineer to the company, I have obtained; and to explain to you the means of executing it, as far as they are determined by the nature of the soil and the levels of the country.

The alluvial land lying below that part of the granite ridge which crosses the peninsula from the ferry opposite to Havre de Grace, reaching the shores of the Delaware at Wilmington, may be considered as a regular inclined plane, sloping gradually to the south-east at the rate of about 6 inches in a mile. Immediately below the granite ridge,—that is, along the foot of Gray's hill, Iron hill, and along the south bank of Christiana creek, which runs parallel to, and close under, the ridge,—its highest inequalties seldom exceed 80 feet, nor does the common surface fall below 70 feet above the tide of the Chesapeake at high water. This plane extends from the granite ridge to the ocean,—and the only considerable depressions to be found in it, are the beds of the land drains, which are worn down into it and produce the appearance of vallies; but there are no insulated hills whatever, and the vallies are merely depressions of the ground below the plane. Hence it is evident, that by going round the heads of the water courses, a line of canal may be found across the peninsula between any two points on the opposite bays, in which the variation of level on the summit will be very small, and that by making the bank out of the spoils of the cut, a canal may be made at the smallest possible expense of digging and removing earth, and at no expense whatever for works of masonry, excepting at each end, where the descent requires the con. struction of locks. For by following the ridge divid- ing the waters which drain into opposite creeks, the necessity of culverts and aqueducts may be wholly avoided. The soil is also of the kind most easily cut, being generally of a sandy loam on and near the sur· face, and beds of good clay are found in abundance for all purposes of puddling.

The advantage of so level and soft a surface for the cut is counterbalanced by the total absence of water to supply it. This circumstance is very im- portant in determining the choice of the line of the canal, among so many that are equally practicable; for as all its water must be brought from the higher grounds upon the ridge, its location ought to be as near to the ridge as possible, in order that the feeder being short, the leakage and evaporation of a long feeder may be avoided. The location of the two ends of the canal does not, however, entirely depend upon its general course along the summit; and a great va- riety of terminations have been proposed, as equally eligible, both on the Chesapeake and the Delaware side. The former, after long and careful examina- tion, has been decided in favor of Welch point, where there has, within the memory of man, been no diminution in the depth of the water, which is below the deposit of alluvium from Elk creek, and where the water is so wide and so deep, as to furnish a very capacious basin for many years to come, for the inconsiderable land wash of Back creek and the small drains in the neighbourhood. But on the Delaware side much difference of opinion has pre- vailed. The summit level of the canal in every case must reach the principal road leading from Christiana bridge down the peninsula, near a tavern called the Bear. This place is only two miles distant from Hamburg or Red hook, on the bay of Newcastle, and a cheap and short cut might be made to either of these points, especially to Red hook, did not two con- siderations forbid it,—the broad and wild water of the bay, and its shallowness at a great distance from the shore, there being only 4 feet 6 inches at low water. Newcastle, is the next eligible point. Newcastle is situated on a prominent point, which is swept both by the flood and the ebb tide. There will therefore be always deep water at the *outer* wharves and piers at that place, and less than 21 feet has not been found on the outside of any of the piers lately erected; or formerly, and even at present, at the wharves, excepting only where the eddy occasioned by the piers has accumulated soft banks of mud.

There could not be a moment's hesitation in fixing the termination of the canal at Newcastle, unless the following reasons should be thought to outweigh the advantages of the best water in the Delaware, and the shortest navigation across the peninsula, which this point offers. It is in the first place feared, that in time of war, when the canal would be invaluable as a means of conveyance of military stores and bodies of men, an enemy's ship of war might destroy the works at Newcastle in a sudden incursion, and return to sea, before the mischief could be prevented. It is further urged, that the mouth of the canal on the river below the tide would be liable to be filled up, in a very short time, as are all places on the Delaware where there is an eddy.— And it is also alledged, that Newcastle is situated so far below Philadelphia (33 miles), that unless with a favorable wind, dull sailing vessels cannot reach Newcastle in one tide, when they might reach the mouth of Christiana, 4 miles higher up the river, and go up the creek with the flood.

The first argument, appears to me to be deserving of consideration in a national point of view, and a small fort would be necessary to defend the mouth of the works against an enemy who should attempt to land, to blow them up. But they could not be injured even by shells beyond the destruction of the gates, which a few hours could put again into repair. To obviate the second objection it would be necessa-

ry to place the tide lock as far out as possible, and to carry out and wharf the side of the canal below the lock as far into the river, as the most projected wharf. The line of the wharves is now limited to 600 feet beyond the lowest street, called Water street, and unless further protruded into the river by a law of the state, this distance presents no formidable difficulty to the work, and places the utmost extension of the wharves, beyond the present time. The third objection is not without foundation. But the narrow and crooked navigation of Christiana creek, presents infinitely more causes of delay than the distance of four miles in the bold navigation of the Delaware. There is however in these objections enough to render it an object of infinite importance both to the nation and to the company, to avail themselves of both the eastern terminations of the canal, and to make a cut also from the Bear to the Christiana creek, about three miles above Wilmington, on a line not altogether so favorable, nor so short as that to New-castle, but presenting no difficulties of importance whatsoever. From the point (Mendenhall's) at which the termination is proposed, 10 feet may be carried out to the river Delaware. The objections to this termination are : the tedious and very crooked navigation of the creek for seven miles to the Delaware. The drawbridge at Wilmington, which must be passed; but more than any other, the opposition of the tides of Delaware and Christiana creek. For if a boat comes into the canal at Welsh point at high water, and passes across in six hours, she will find half flood in Christiana, and must wait the ebb to go down. On her arrival in the Delaware in two and a half or three hours, she will have again to wait three or four hours for the flood to proceed to Philadelphia, or up the Brandywine to the celebrated mills, the interests of which are well worthy of attention. Whereas a vessel arriving at Newcastle and finding the flood tide running, which will always happen if she comes to Welch point with a flood tide, may at once proceed up the Delaware, or up the Brandywine or Christiana creek, without delay. It must also be mentioned, that without a favorable tide, it is difficult to work down the Christiana creek against the wind, which is always unfavorable in some reach or other of its crooked navigation, when on the contrary, there is ample room in the Delaware to use all advantages of wind and tide.

On the other hand, it must be urged in favor of Christiana creek, that there is navigable water for boats drawing 8 feet above the proposed termination of the canal, as far as Christiana bridge, and that the navigation may be pushed still higher;—that the little town of Newport is now the depot of the produce of a very extensive and fruitful country extending into Lancaster county, and is 20 miles nearer to Lancaster than Philadelphia, and that to connect so important a field of productive business immediately with the canal, it may be worth while to incur an encreased expense and some inconvenience and delay in the mere *thoroughfare* navigation : and it may be added, that the large fixed capital of the town of Wilmington, far exceeding that of Newcastle, demands from the good policy, as well as the good will of the company or the nation, some consideration.

Well aware of the thankless task of giving a decisive and honest opinion on either side, I content myself with furnishing the materials of determination to you, and proceed to describe the nature and principles of the work actually executed in the feeder, and proposed for the canal.

Between the waters of the Chesapeake and the Delaware there are three streams which, rising in the high land above the canal, may be brought down to it as feeders, the Christiana creek, the Whiteclay creek, and the Elk itself.

The Elk and the Whiteclay are nearly equal in the regular quantity of water they supply, the Christiana is both smaller and more irregular. The Elk descends in a very crooked and rapid stream, 84 feet in four miles from Elk forge to the tide near Elkton, and unites with the wide water of the Chesapeake at Turkey point. The ridge that seperates its waters from those of the Delaware terminates in a high insulated hill, called Gray's hill, which is united to the high land by a low and narrow ridge, crossing the post road on the boundary line of Delaware and Maryland. The Christiana creek is the first water falling from the high land into the Delaware. It collects all the waters that fall round the high insulated hill called Iron hill, at the N. E. foot of which it turns to the N. E. and, running in that direction under the foot of the granite ridge into the Delaware, receives the Whiteclay, Redclay and Brandywine in its course, and also numerous land drains from the level land to the South East. Of these three streams it has been ascertained that they may all be brought to the canal, but the Elk with the least expense and the shortest cut. The vallies in which they all run having been worn in deep and rocky land, and branching into deep ravines, the beds of rapid rivulets, offer great difficulties to the work necessary to divert their course.

In the Elk feeder, the canal is cut in the rock for about half a mile; embankments are made across several vallies, but the principal difficulty and expense consisted in cutting through a tongue of high land called Bellhill, through which the digging is 30 feet for near half a mile, and again through the dividing ridge, to the depth of 25 feet for above half that distance; these two difficulties have been conquered. Another smaller hill remains to be cut through, but it may be avoided by a circuitous cut, much less expensive, but also much less eligible. On the Delaware side of the ridge, the feeder is cut through a swampy flat of more than a mile in length, while the descent is only six inches. The general elevation of this flat is 86 feet above the tide, and as the head of the feeder at Elk forge is only 84 feet, it could have little descent, and falls only 2 inches in a mile. It has on this account been made a spacious canal of 3 feet 6 inches water, 22 feet 6 inches on the surface, and 12 feet at the bottom, affording as far as it goes a good and valuable inland navigation. The feeder is 6 miles in length; at the end of 5 miles is a lock for the passage of boats, and a side cut to communicate with the reservoir. A contiguous valley offers the means of making a reservoir, of more than a hundred acres. It has been proposed to embank 30 acres for this purpose. The lock is of 10 feet lift. The reservoir will be level with the upper feeder, of course 10 feet above the level of the canal, and under such a head will give the canal a plenteous and rapid supply as it is wanted. Below the lock the feeder is 5 feet deep, and 27 feet on the surface of the water: it will join the canal about a mile west of Aikentown. In the construction of the feeder permanence has been a very principal consideration. All the culverts are of solid masonry; no land water can run into the cut; the banks are sloped as 2 to 3; the embankments are well puddled, and the piers of the bridges are of hewn stone.

From the description which I have given of the soil of the peninsula, it is evident that the amount of digging constitutes the chief expense of the canal. To lessen this amount and to shorten the canal, it is proposed to quit the level in three places, and to cross three land drains that lead into Christiana creek, one at Aikentown, and two between Aikentown and the Bear. Small aqueducts and short embankments only are necessary to effect this. If the canal should terminate at Newcastle, a narrow marsh must also be crossed,—if at Christiana, deeper cutting must be encountered.

But neither of these difficulties increase the expense of the canal more than $ 7,500 each, beyond that of the same length of the general cut.

On all other points the report of the committee

furnishes ample information; and I will only add,—
that neither in Europe, nor in our own country do I
know a line of inland navigation, which by so short a
distance, and at so easy an expense, unites such extensive and productive ranges of commercial intercourse.

With the highest respect,

I am yours,

(Signed)   B. H. LATROBE.

ALBERT GALLATIN, Esq.
Secretary of the Treasury.

—◼:✷:◼—

April 1, 1808.

POSTSCRIPT.

IN the questions proposed to me by you, the
subject of artificial roads was comprehended. But
being informed by you that the canal companies of
Pennsylvania and Maryland, had transmitted to you
ample accounts of their undertakings, and as in their
works, experience has taught a system and mode of
execution, of the most perfect kind; I have refrain-
ed from adding any thing to the information thus
acquired. It has however occurred to me, that a few
remarks upon rail roads might not be unacceptable to
you, especially as the public attention has been often
called to this sort of improvement, and the public
mind filled with very imperfect conceptions of its
utility.

Rail roads may be constructed of iron or of timber. The most durable (but also the most expensive) rail roads, consist of cast iron *rails* let down on
stone foundations; such roads will last for ages. Cast

iron rails secured on beds of timber, are sufficiently durable for our country, and of moderate expense. Rail roads entirely of timber, are fit only for temporary puropses.

A rail road consists of two pair of parallel ways, one pair for going, the other for returning carriages: single roads with occasional passing places, are applicable to some situations, and are of course less expensive. I will concisely describe the road best adapted to the objects that in our country can be attained by it:—*The rails* are of cast iron, and consist of a tread and a flanch, forming in their section the letter ⌐ The tread is 3 inches wide, the flanch 2 inches high. The rails need not be more than ⅝ of an inch *average* thickness, and they may be cast in lengths of 5 to 6 feet each; each rail will, at six feet length, contain 225 cubic inches, which, at 4 inches to the pound, is 56 lb. each rail, or 1 cwt. for every 6 feet in length of the road, or 44 ton per mile.

In order to form a road of these rails, they must be laid at the distance of from 3 1-2 to 5 feet (according to the carriage that is to run upon them) parallel to each other; the ends of every two pair of rails being let and pinned down into a piece of timber lying across the roads, the holes for the pins must *be cast* in the rails. These pieces of timber may be of any form, provided they are level at the top, and they cannot be a great part of the expense of the road in any situation. The most durable timber is certainly the best: but no timber can be very durable in the situation it must occupy on the surface, and partly or wholly covered with earth. The perfection of the road consists in the parallel rails being laid perfectly level with each other across the road, and perfectly jointed. In most parts of the union the rails could, I think, be delivered at from 80 to $ 90 per ton, and in many at $ 60—but taking $ 80 as the average on the spot, the road will cost—-

Rails delivered, 44 ton, at $ 80,   3,520
Levelling the road, very uncertain, but I will
    suppose as an average for levelling and
    filling in with good gravel or broken stone,
    $ 2 50 per perch, or per mile, - -   800
Timber and bedding at 50 per rail, -   440
Incidents and superintendance, - -   240

                                5,000
For a set of returning ways, - -   5,000

        Total per mile, - - $ 10,000

    The carriages which travel on these roads may
be of various dimensions, agreeably to the material
to be conveyed, and the necessary angle of the road.
They have low cast iron wheels fast upon the axle,
which turns round. Thus, the two wheels on the
axle making the same number of revolutions in the
same space of time, the carriage necessarily goes
straight forward, and cannot be thrown off the ways
by any small obstruction on one side.

    The principle upon which such astonishing loads
may be drawn on the ways by a single horse, is
the dimunition of friction in the greatest possible degree. On a good rail road, descending under an
angle of only one degree, one horse may draw
eight tons in 4 waggons of two tons each without difficulty. The astonishing loads drawn upon
rail roads by single horses in England, have in-
duced many of our citizens to hope for their early
application to the use of our country. I fear this
hope is vain, excepting on a very small scale,
and that chiefly in the coal country near Richmond.
For it is evident that upon a rail road no other carriage but that which is expressly constructed for the
purpose, can be employed,—and that to render a rail
road sufficiently saving of the expense of common
carriage, to justify the cost of its erection, there must

be a very great demand for its use. But the sort of produce which is carried to our markets is collected from such scattered points, and comes by such a diversity of routes, that rail roads are out of the question as to the carriage of common articles. Rail roads leading from the coal mines to the margin of James river, might answer their expense, or others from the marble quarries near Philadelphia to the Schuylkill. But these are the only instances within my knowledge, in which they at present might be employed.

There is, however, a use for rail roads as a temporary means of overcoming the most difficult parts of artificial navigation, and for this use they are invaluable, and in many instances offer the means of accomplishing distant lines of communication which might otherwise remain impracticable, even to our national resources, for centuries to come.

Mr. Fulton's Communication.

(F)

SIR,

BY your letter of the 29th of July, I am happy to find that the attention of Congress is directing itself towards the opening of communications through the United States, by means of roads and canals; and it would give me particuliar pleasure to aid you with useful informaion on such works, as I have long been contemplating their importance in many points of view.

But a year has not yet elapsed since I returned to America, and my private concerns have occupied so much of my time, that as yet I have acquired but very little local information on the several canals which have been commenced.

Such information, however, is perhaps at present not the most important branch of the subject, particularly as it can be obtained in a few months at a small expense, whenever the public mind shall be impressed with a sense of the vast advantages of a general system of cheap conveyance.

I hope, indeed, that every intelligent American will in a few years, be fully convinced of the necessity of such works to promote the national wealth, and his individual interest. Such conviction must arise from that habit of reflection which accompanies the republican principle, and points out their true interest on subjects of political economy. From such reflections arises their love of agriculture and the useful arts, knowing them to augmeut the riches and happiness of the nation; hence also their dislike to standing armies and military navies, as being the means of increasing the proportion of non-productive individuals, whose labor is not only lost, but who must be supported out of the produce of the industrious inhabitants, and diminish their enjoyments.

Such right thinking does great honor to our nation, and leads forward to the highest possible state of civilization, by directing the powers of man from useless and destructive occupations, to pursuits which multiply the productions of useful labor, and create abundance.

Though such principles actuate our citizens, they are not yet in every instance, aware of their best interests; nor can it be expected that they should perceive at once the advantages of those plans of improvement which are still new in this country. Hence the most useful works have sometimes been opposed; and we are not without examples of men being elected into the state legislatures for the express purpose of preventing roads, canals and bridges being constructed. But in such errors of judgment our countrymen have not been singular. When a bill was brought into the British parliament 50 years ago, to establish turnpike roads throughout the kingdom, the inhabitants for 40 miles round London petitioned against such roads; their arguments were, that good roads would enable the farmers of the interior country to bring their produce to the London market cheaper than they who lived nearer the city and paid higher rent; that the market would be overstocked, the prices diminished and they unable to pay their rent, or obtain a living. The good sense of parliament, however, prevailed; the roads were made, the population and commerce of London increased, the demand for produce increased, and he who lived nearest to London still had a superior advantage in the market.

In like manner I hope the good sense of our legislature will prevail over the ignorance and prejudice which may still exist against canals. And here an important question occurs, which it may be proper to examine with some attention in this early stage of our public improvements,—whether, as a system, we should prefer canals to turnpike roads? Our habits are in favor of roads; and few of us have conceived any better method of opening communications to the various parts of the states. But in China and Holland, canals are more numerous than roads ; in those countries the inhabitants are accustomed to see all their productions carried either on natural or artificial canals, and they would be as much at a loss to know how we, as a civilized people, could do without such means of conveyance, as we are surprised at their perseverance and ingenuity in making them.* England, France, and the principal states of Europe commenced their improvements with roads; but as the science of the engineer improved, and civilization advanced, canals were introduced, and England and France are now making every exertion to get the whole of their heavy productions waterborne, for they have become sensible of the vast superiority of canals over roads.

Our system perhaps ought to embrace them both : Canals for the long carriage of the whole materials of agriculture and manufactures, and roads for travelling and the more numerous communications of the country. With these two modes in contemplation, when public money is to be expended with a view to the greatest good, we should now consider which object is entitled to our first attention. Shall we begin with canals, which will carry the farmer's produce cheap to market, and return him merchandize at reduced prices ? Or shall we first make roads to accommodate travellers, and let the produce of our farms, mines and forests, labor under such heavy expenses that they cannot come to market ?

To throw some light on this interesting question, I will base my calculations on the Lancaster turnpike road. There the fair experiment has been made to penetrate from Philadelphia to the interior country, and the mode of calculation here given will serve for drawing comparisons on the utility of roads and

---

* The royal canal from Canton to Pekin, is 825 miles long, its breadth 30 feet, its depth 9 feet.

canals, for all the great leading communications of America.

From Philadelphia to the Susquehannah at Columbia, is 74 miles; that road if I am rightly informed, cost on an average, 6,000 dollars a mile, or 444,000 for the whole. On it, from Columbia to Philadelphia, a barrel of flour, say 200 weight, pays one dollar carriage. A broad wheeled waggon carries 30 barrels or 3 tons, and pays for turnpike 3 dollars; thus for each ton carried the turnpike company receives only one dollar.

I will now suppose a canal to have been cut from Philadelphia to Columbia, and with its windings to make 100 miles, at 15,000 dollars* a mile, or for the whole 1,500,000 dollars. On such canal, *one man,* *one boy* and *horse*, would convey 25 tons 20 miles a day,† on which the following would be the expenses:

One man, - - - - -	1 00
One horse, - • - - -	1 00
One boy, - - - - -	50
Tolls for repairing the canal, - - -	1 00
Tolls for passing locks, inclined planes, tunnels and aqueducts, - - -	1 00
Interest on the wear of the boat, - -	50
Total,	$ 5 00

This is equal to 20 cents a ton for 20 miles, and no more than one dollar a ton for 100 miles, instead of 10 dollars paid by the road. Consequently for each ton carried from Columbia to Philadelphia on the canal, the company might take a toll of six dol-

* On averaging the canals of America, 15,000 dollars a mile will be abundantly sufficient to construct them in the best manner, particularly if made on the inclined plane principle, with small boats, each carrying 6 tons.

† One horse will draw on a canal, from 25 to 50 tons, 20 miles in one day. I have stated the least they ever do, and the highest rate of charges, that no deception may enter into these calculations.

lars instead of one, which is now got by the road, and then the flour would arrive at Philadelphia for 7 dollars a ton instead of 10, which it now pays. The merchandize would also arrive at Columbia from Philadelphia, for three dollars a ton less than is now paid; which cheap carriage both ways would not only benefit the farmer and merchant, but would draw more commerce on the canal than now moves on the road, and thereby add to the profits of the company.

But to proceed with my calculations, I will suppose that exactly the same number of tons would move on the canal that are now transported by the road. Again, let it be supposed that at one dollar a ton the turnpike company gains five per cent. per annum on their capital of 444,000 dollars, or 22,200 dollars, consequently 22,200 tons must be carried, which at six dollars a ton to the canal company, would have given 133,200 dollars a year, or 8 1-2 per cent. for their capital of 1,500,000 dollars.

The reason of this vast difference in the expense of carriage by roads or canals, will be obvious to any one who will take the trouble to reflect, that on a road of the best kind four horses, and sometimes five, are necessary to transport only three tons. On a canal one horse will draw 25 tons, and thus perform the work of 40 horses; the saving therefore is in the value of the horses, their feeding, shoeing, geer, waggons, and attendance. These facts should induce companies to consider well their interest, when contemplating an enterprise of this sort, and what would be their profits, not only in interest for their capital, but the benefit which their lands would receive by the cheap carriage of manure and of their productions.

In considering the profit to accrue to a company from a canal instead of roads, there is another important calculation to be made, and for that purpose I will proceed with the Lancaster turnpike, supposing it to extend to Pittsburg, 320 miles. On which

the carriage being at the rate now paid from Columbia to Philadelphia, that is 10 dollars a ton for
74 miles, the ton from Pittsburgh would amount to
42 dollars, at which price a barrel of flour would
cost 4 dollars in carriage, an expense which excludes
it from the market. Thus grain, the most important
and abundant production of our interior country,
and which should give vigor to our manufactures, is
shut up in the districts most favorable to its culture;
or to render it portable and convert it into cash, it
must be distilled to brutalize and poison society. In
like manner all heavy articles of little monied value,
can only move within the narrow limits of 100 miles;
but were a canal made the whole distance, and by
one or more companies, they might arrange the tolls
in the following manner, so as to favor the long carriage of heavy articles.

The expense of man, boy and horse, as before
stated, would cost only 3 dollars to boat one ton of
flour 300 miles, this is 30 cents a barrel; suppose
then, that the company receive 70 cents a barrel or 7
dollars a ton, flour could then come from Pittsburgh
to Philadelphia for one dollar a barrel, the sum which
is now paid from Columbia; thus the canal company
would gain $ 7 a ton by a trade which could never
move through a road of equal length. Here we see
that on canals the tolls may be so arranged as to
draw to them articles of little monied value, and it
would be the interest of the company or companies to
make such regulations. But on turnpike roads no such
accommodation of charges in proportion to distance,
can be effected, because of the number of horses
which cannot be dispensed with.* Even were the
roads made at the public expense and toll free, still the
carriage of one ton for 300 miles would cost at least

---

* In my work on small canals, published in 1796, page 140, there is a
table shewing a mode of regulating the boating and tonnage in such manner, that a ton may be transported 1300 miles for 5 dollars. Yet by this
method canal companies would gain more toll than by any other means
yet practised.

35 dollars. But were canals made at the public expense, and no other toll demanded than should be sufficient to keep them in repair, a ton in boating and tolls would only cost 3 dollars for 300 miles; and for 35 dollars, the sum which must be paid to carry one ton 300 miles on the best of roads, it could be boated *three thousand five hundred miles*, and draw resources from the centre of this vast continent.

But striking as this comparison is, I will still extend it. The merchandize which can bear the expense of carriage on our present roads to Pittsburgh, Kentucky, Tennessee, or any other distance of 300 miles, and which for that distance pays 100 dollars a ton, could be boated on canals *ten thousand miles for that sum.*

As these calculations are founded on facts which will not be denied by any one acquainted with the advantages of canals, it is the interest of every man of landed property, and particularly of the farmers of the back countries, that canals should be immediately constructed and rendered as numerous as the funds of the nation will permit, and the present population requires; and as inhabitants multiply most towards the interior and must extend westward, still moving more distant from the sea coast and the market for their produce, it is good policy and right that canals should follow them. In 25 years our population will amount to 14 millions; two-thirds of whom will spread over the western countries. Suppose then that 3,500,000 dollars were annually appropriated to canals, such a sum would pay for 300 miles of canal each year, and in 20 years we should have 6000 miles circulating through and penetrating into the interior of the different states; such sums, though seemingly large, and such works, though apparently stupendous, are not more than sufficient to keep pace with the rapid increase of our population, to open a market and carry to every district such foreign articles as we near the coast enjoy. With this view of the subject, arises a political question of the utmost magnitude to these states—which is—

That as our national debt diminishes, and the treasury increases in surplus revenue, will it not be the best interest of the people to continue the present duties on imports, and expend the products in national improvements ?

To illustrate this question, I will state some examples of the rate of duties and the expense of carriage, to prove that by keeping on the duties and making canals with the revenue, goods in a great number of instances will be cheaper to the consumer, than by taking off the duties, and leaving the transport to roads.

FIRST EXAMPLE :

Brown sugar pays in duty, two and a half cents
    a lb. or for 100 lb. -   -   .   - $2 50
It pays for waggoning 300 miles,   -   - 5 00

                        Total, $7 50

By the canal, it would cost in boating 15 cents for 300 miles ; consequently the boating and duty would amount to $2 65 ; therefore, by keeping on the duty and making canals, sugar would arrive at the interior, 300 miles, for $2 35 the hundred weight cheaper than if the duties were taken off and the transport left to roads.

SECOND EXAMPLE :

One bushel of salt, weighing 56lb. paid in
    duty,   -   -   -   -   -   - $0 20
To carry it 300 miles by roads, the expense is 2 50

                        Total, $2 70

By the canal it would cost for boating 300 miles, seven and a half cents. By keeping on the duties and making the canals, it would arrive to the interior consumer at $2 32 1-2 the bushel cheaper than were the duties taken off, and the transport left to roads.

THIRD EXAMPLE:

Molasses pays 5 cents a gallon duty, this is for
100 lb. - - - - - - $0 75
It pays for waggoning 300 miles, - 5 00
                                       ————
                              Total, $5 75

By the canal the carriage would cost 15 cents, and it would arrive at the interior, at $4 10 the hundred weight, or 27 cents a gallon cheaper than were the duties taken off, and the transport left to roads.

Numerous other articles might be stated to shew that the real mode of rendering them cheap to the interior consumer, is to keep on the duties and facilitate the carriage with the funds so raised. These, however, may be considered as partial benefits, and not sufficiently general to warrant keeping on the duties. But there is a point of view in which I hope it will appear that the advantages are general, and will be felt throughout every part of the states. It is by reducing the expense of all kinds of carriage, and thus economise to each individual more than he now pays in duty on the foreign articles which he consumes.

FOR EXAMPLE:

Wood, for fuel, is an article of the first necessity; it cannot bear the expense of transport 20 miles on roads; at that distance it is shut out from the market, and the price of fuel is consequently raised the amount of the carriage; were a cord of wood carried 20 miles on roads, it would pay for waggoning at least 3 dollars; on a canal it would pay 20 cents; thus, on only one cord of wood, there is an economy of $2 80,—which economy would pay the duty on 14 pounds of tea, at 20 cents the lb. duty;

Or 140 pounds of sugar, at 2 cents the lb. duty ;
Or 56 pounds of coffee, at 5 cents the lb. duty ;
Or 14 bushels of salt, at 20 cents the bushel duty ;
Or 56 gallons of molasses, at 5 cents the gallon duty.

I will now suppose a city of 50,000 inhabitants, who for their household and other uses will consume 50 thousand cord a year, on which there would be an economy of 140,000 dollars, a sum in all probability equal to the duties paid by the inhabitants. For the duties divided on the whole of the American people, are but $2 28 to each individval. Here I have estimated each person to pay $2 80, yet this estimate is made on one cord of wood to each inhabitant of a city ; were I to calculate the economy on the carriage of building timber, lime, sand, bricks, stone, iron, flour, corn, provisions and materials of all kinds which enter or go out of a city, it would be five times this sum ; and thus the towns and cities are to be benefited. The farmer or miller who lives 20 miles from a market, pays at least 22 cents to waggon a barrel of flour that distance ; by the canal it would cost 2 cents ; the economy would be 20 cents ; at 100 miles the economy would be 100 cents, and at 150 miles it would be 150 cents ; beyond this distance flour cannot come to market by roads ; yet at this distance the economy of 150 cents on the carriage of one barrel of flour would pay the duty on

7 1-2 pounds of tea ;
Or 75 pounds of sugar ;
Or 30 pounds of coffee ;
Or 7 1-2 bushels of salt ;
Or 30 gallons of molasses.

Thus it is, that the benefits arising from a good system of canals, are general and mutual. Therefore should peace and the reduction of the national debt, give an overflowing treasury, I hope you, and the majority of Americans, will think with me, that the duties should not be taken off nor diminished ; for such an act, instead of relieving the people, would really oppress them, by destroying the means of reducing the expense of transport, and of opening to them a cheap mode of arriving at good markets.

To proceed with these demonstrations, let us look at the rich productions of our interior country :

Wheat, flour, oats, barley, beans, grain, and pulse of all kinds ;

Cyder, apples, and fruits of all kinds ;

Salt, salted beef, pork ond other meats ;*

Hides, tallow, beeswax ;

Cast and forged iron ;

Pot and pearl ashes, tanners' bark ;

Tar, pitch, rosin and turpentine ;

Hemp, flax and wool ;

Plaister of paris, so necessary to our agriculture ;

Coals, and potters' earth for our manufactures ;

Marble, lime and timber for our buildings.

All these articles are of the first necessity, but few of them can bear the expense of 5 dollars the hundred weight to be transported 300 miles on roads. Yet on canals they would cost in boating only 15 cents the 100 weight for that distance.

There is another great advantage to individuals and the nation arising from canals, which roads can never give. It is that when a canal runs through a long line of mountainous country, such as the greater part of the interior of America, all the ground below for half a mile or more may be watered and converted into meadow and other profitable culture.

How much these conveniences of irrigation will add to the produce of agriculture and the beauties of nature, I leave to experienced farmers and agricultural societies to calculate.

In Italy and Spain it is the practice to sell water out of the canals, for watering meadows and other

---

* Animals are now driven to market 300 or more miles, at a considerable expense and loss of flesh, for two principal reasons . first, the expense of transporting the salt to the interior ; and second, the expense of carrying the salted meats to market.

lands. In such cases tubes are put into the canal, under the pressure of a certain head of water, and suffered to run a given time for a fixed price; the monies thus gained add much to the emoluments of the canal companies.

But with all these immense advantages which canals give, it may be a question with many individuals, whether they can be constucted in great leading lines from our sea coast and navigable rivers, to the frontiers of the several states, or pass our mountains and penetrate to the remote parts of our interior country. Should doubts arise on this part of the plan, I beg leave to assure you that there is no difficulty in carrying canals over our highest mountains, and even where nature has denied us water. For water is always to be found in the valleys, and the canal can be constructed to the foot of the mountain, carrying the water to that situation. Should there be no water on the mountain or its sides, there will be wood or coals; either or both of which can be brought cheap to the works by means of the canal. Then with steam engines the upper ponds of canal can be filled from the lower levels, and with the engines the boats can on inclined planes be drawn from the lower to the upper canal. For this mode of operating it is necessary to have small boats of six tons each. As the steam engines are to draw up and let down the boats on inclined planes, no water is drawn from the upper level of canal as when locks are used. Consequently when the upper ponds have been once filled, it is only necessary that the engine should supply leakage and evaporation. There is another mode of supplying the leakage and evaporation of the higher levels: On the tops and sides of mountains there are hollows or ravines which can be banked at the lower extremity, thus forming a reservoir to catch the rain or melted snow. From such reservoirs the ponds of canal can be replenished in the dry months of summer. This mode of reserving water is in practice in England for canals, and in Spain for irrigation. In this manner I will suppose it necessary to pass a mountain 800 feet high; then four inclined planes each of 200 feet rise, would gain the summit, and four would descend on the other side.—Total 8 inclined planes and 8 steam engines. Each steam engine of 12 horse power would cost about ten thousand dollars, in all 80,000 dollars; each would burn about 12 bushels of coal in 12 hours, or 96 bushels for the 8 engines for one day's work.

The coals in such situations may be estimated at

12 cents a bushel, or - -	$ 11 52
At each engine and inclined plane there must be 5 men—total 40 men, at one dollar each, -	40
Total	**$ 51 52**

For this sum they could pass 500 tons in one day over the 8 inclined planes, which for each ton is only - - - - 10 cents.

Suppose the mountain to be 20 miles' wide, boating for each ton would cost 20 do.

Total 30 cents

a ton for passing over the mountain, which will be more or less according to circumstances. These calculations being only intended to remove any doubts which may arise on the practicability of passing our mountains—

Having thus in some degree considered the advantages which canals will produce in point of wealth to individuals and the nation, I will now consider their importance to the union and their political consequences.

First, their effect on raising the value of the public lands, and thereby augmenting the revenue.

In all cases where canals shall pass through the lands of the United States, and open a cheap communication to a good market, such lands will rise in value for 20 miles on each side of the canal. The farmer who will reside 20 miles from the canal can in one day carry a load of produce to its borders. And were the lands 600 miles from one of our seaport towns his barrel of flour, in weight 200 lb. could be carried that distance for 60 cents, the price which is now paid to carry a barrel 50 miles on the Lancaster turnpike. Consequently, as relates to cheapness of carriage, and easy access to market, the new lands which lie 600 miles from the sea ports, would be of equal value with lands of equal fertility which are 50 miles from the sea ports. But not to insist on their being of so great value until population is as great, it is evident that they must rise in value in a 3 or 4 fold degree, every lineal mile of canal would accommodate 25,600 acres. The lands sold by the United States in 1806, averaged about 2 dollars an acre, and certainly every acre accommodated with a canal, would produce 6 dollars; thus only 20 miles of canal each year, running through national lands, would raise the value of 512,000 acres at least 4 dollars an acre, giving 2,048,000 dollars to the treasury, a sum sufficient to make 136 miles of canal. Had an individual such a property, and funds to construct canals to its centre, he certainly would do it for his own interest. The nation has the property, and the nation possesses ample funds for such undertakings.

Second, on their effect in cementing the union, and extending the principles of confederated republican government. Numerous have been the speculations on the duration of our union, and intrigues have been practised to sever the western from the eastern states. The opinion endeavored to be inculcated, was, that the inhabitants beyond the mountains were cut off from the market of the Atlantic states; that consequently they had a separate interest, and should use their resources to open a communication to a market of their own; that remote from the seat of government they could not enjoy their portion of advantages arising from the union, and that sooner or later they must separate and govern for themselves.

Others by drawing their examples from European governments, and the monarchies which have grown out of the feudal habits of nations of warriors, whose minds were bent to the absolute power of the few, and the servile obedience of the many, have conceived these states of too great an extent to continue united under a republican form of government, and that the time is not distant when they will divide into little kingdoms, retrograding from common sense to ignorance, adopting all the follies and barbarities which are every day practised in the kingdoms and petty states of Europe. But those who have reasoned in this way, have not reflected that men are the creatures of habit, and that their habits as well as their interests may be so combined, as to make it impossible to separate them without falling back into a state of barbarism. Although in ancient times some specks of civilization have been effaced by hordes of uncultivated men, yet it is remarkable that since the invention of printing and general diffusion of knowledge, no nation has retrograded in science or improvements; nor is it reasonable to suppose that the Americans, who have as much, if not more information in general, than any other people, will ever abandon an advantage which they have once gained. England, which at one time was seven petty kingdoms, has by habit long been united into one. Scotland by succession became united to England, and is now bound to her by habit, by turnpike roads, canals and reciprocal interests. In like manner all the counties of England, or departments of France, are bound to each other; and when the United States shall be bound together by canals, by cheap and easy access to market in all directions, by a sense of mutual interests arising from mutual intercourse and mingled commerce; it will be no more possible to split them into independent and separate governments, each lining its frontiers with fortifications and troops, to shackle their own exports and imports to and from the neighboring states; than it is now possible for the government of England to divide and form again into seven kingdoms.

But it is necessary to bind the states together by the people's interests, one of which is to enable every man to sell the produce of his labor at the best market and purchase at the cheapest. This accords with the idea of Hume, "that the government of a wise "people would be little more than a system of civil "police; for the best interest of man is industry and "a free exchange of the produce of his labor for the "things which he may require."

On this humane principle, what stronger bonds of union can be invented than those which enable each individual to transport the produce of his industry 12,00 miles for 60 cents the hundred weight? Here then is a certain method of securing the union of the states, and of rendering it as lasting as the continent we inhabit.

It is now eleven years that I have had this plan in contemplation for the good of our country. At the conclusion of my work on small canals, there is a letter to Thos. Mifflin, then governor of the state of Pennsylvania, on a system of canals for America. In it I contemplated the time when "*canals should pass* "*through every vale, wind round each hill and bind* "*the whole country together in the bonds of social in-* "*tercourse;*" and I am now happy to find that through the good management of a wise administration, a period has arrived when an overflowing treasury exhibits abundant resources, and points the mind to works of such immense importance.

Hoping speedily to see them become favorite objects with the whole American people,

I have the honor to be
Your most obedient,

ROBERT FULTON.

To ALBERT GALLATIN, ESQ.
Secretary of the Treasury.

Washington, Dec. 8, 1807.